In Search of Sanity

IN SEARCH OF SANITY

A CHRONICLE OF THE CANADIAN
MENTAL HEALTH ASSOCIATION
1918-1988

JOHN D. GRIFFIN
MA, MD, DPM (ENG), FRCP (C)

third eye
London   Canada
1989

In Search of Sanity
© 1989 John D. Griffin

Canadian Cataloguing in Publication Data

Griffin, John D. (John Douglas), 1906-
    In Search of Sanity

Bibliography: P
Includes index
ISBN 0-919581-50-1

1. Canadian Mental Health Association - History.
2. Mental Health - Canada - History. 1. Title.

RA790.AIC35 1988   362.2'06'071 C88 - 095224 - 5

Published by
Third Eye Publications Inc.
31 Clarke Side Road
London Ontario Canada
N5W 5W5

JOHN D. GRIFFIN   *IN SEARCH OF SANITY*

Dedication

Astonishing progress has been made over the past fifty years in removing the last vestige of the old asylum era. But we cannot claim that all Canadians suffering from mental illness are being treated with compassion and respect. An unrelenting struggle against ignorance and prejudice is still necessary to ensure the provision of truly effective mental health services. A constant source of strength and encouragement in this struggle over many years is the dedication of many thousands of citizens who have, with skill and persistence, supported the work of the *Canadian Mental Health Association.* This brief history is therefore affectionately dedicated to all these volunteers, past, present, and future.

The publication of this document was made possible by a grant from the Community Mental Health Branch, Ministry of Health, Province of Ontario, Canada.

Foreword

Jack Griffin has dedicated this book to the thousands of volunteers, past, present, and future, who are the heart and soul of the Canadian Mental Health Association.

As the current volunteer President of CMHA, and on behalf of the Board of Directors and membership, I should like to say how delighted we are that this book reflects the author's lifelong commitment to the organization including since his retirement as General Director in 1971, the time which he has spent preparing this document.

Jack Griffin is a twentieth century pioneer. He is the only person who could have written this history. It is a tribute to his own life's work.

E. Austin Fricker,
National President,
Canadian Mental Health Association.

CONTENTS

Preface

X

Appendices

XIII

Preface

The Canadian Mental Health Association, formerly the Canadian National Committee for Mental Hygiene, is one of the oldest continuing voluntary health organizations in Canada. A constellation of factors stimulated its origin and its development. In the early days of the 20th century, leaders in the field of maternal and child health, such as Dr. Helen MacMurchy campaigned for the care of the feeble-minded, now called the Developmentally Handicapped. At about the same time, educators were advocating the establishment of special classes and improved institutional care for 'backward' pupils. Concerned citizens joined with the professionals in lobbying the government to do something about the "menace of the feeble-minded."

With the advent of the First World War it became obvious that, because of mental retardation and emotional instability, many potential recruits were unfit for military service. However, due to the lack of adequate screening procedures, the incidence of mental breakdown in the Canadian Armed Forces, at home and overseas, was very high. As the war progressed the casualties included an increasing number of "shell-shock" cases. Despite the widespread belief that this condition was caused by concussion due to exploding shells, the medical community soon recognized that "shell-shock" was a functional nervous disorder usually associated with stress. Due to the lack of better facilities, many soldiers with psychiatric disorders were placed in provincial mental hospitals which, with few exceptions, were run-down, over-crowded and under-staffed. Eventually, the military authorities became concerned about the plight of its veterans who were relegated to these unfortunate places.

Co-incidentally, Dr. C.M. Hincks and Dr. C.K. Clarke, encouraged by Clifford Beers of New Haven, began to organize the Canadian Committee for Mental Hygiene which was founded early in 1918.

In 1968 the organization celebrated its fiftieth anniversary, and the National Board of Directors began thinking of preparing an historical review. There was considerable interest in recording the changing picture of the care, treatment, and prevention of mental illness and particularly the role the Association had played in effecting these changes. For various reasons, mostly related to the availability of personnel, space, and a modest budget, work did not begin on this project until 1980.

The history of a voluntary philanthropic movement provides interesting material for study. The aims and objectives change over the years. Leaders emerge and disappear, volunteers are recruited, develop interest and enthusiasm, and sometimes become disenchanted. The organization divides into local and regional divisions, and often encounters difficulties because of competition. Conflicts and confrontations appear with disagreement on staff, program, and financing. Some organizations survive these difficulties, others change or disappear entirely. The Canadian Mental Health Association is no exception. It has experienced these problems, and yet for over sixty years it has survived and continues to grow in public recognition and national support.

By the end of the 19th century, the problems posed by mental illness and mental health seemed relatively simple. There were the obviously insane - the lunatics, the idiots, and the feeble-minded - and there were those who were sane, obviously neither lunatic nor idiotic. The major problem concerned those with serious mental disorders and involved providing humane care, protection, and wherever possible medical treatment and social re-education. The objectives of a voluntary mental health association reflected these simple goals - to promote the building of more comfortable institutions; to provide better food and care; to hire more staff and more competent doctors; and to start working on the possibility of prevention. Scientific research on the causes of insanity and on new and better methods of treatment was to be encouraged but, obviously the major emphasis at first was on the improvement of physical facilities and services. Volunteers had a role to play in visiting the institutions, providing social programs and comforts, and possibly in helping discharged patients adjust to life in the community. But even this type of volunteerism did not evolve in any organized national program until the middle of the 1950s.

For the first half of the 20th century, the problems of the mental health services remained essentially the same. The trends were toward larger and hopefully better institutions, more beds, more staff, larger budgets, and gradually better medical, psychiatric, and psychological care. Outpatient clinics, both stationary and travelling, appeared in connection with the provincial services during the late 1920s. Research into new treatments began in the '30s. The last twenty-five years, however, have seen obvious and sometimes dramatic changes. Some of these are the reduction by more than 75% of the number of hospital beds utilized for the care and treatment of the mentally ill in provincial institutions; the development of a new range of drugs for the treatment of mental disorders; the increase in the number of community mental health clinics and centres including the psychiatric units in general hospitals; the increase in the number of psychiatrists engaged in institutional and private practice together with the increase in the number of non-medical specialists representing several disciplines active in types of therapy; and, finally, the provision of government and tax-supported health insurance to cover costs of hospital care and medical (including psychiatric) treatment.

Developments of this kind should be regarded as positive steps. Furthermore, it is understandable if those engaged in organized voluntary work in the mental health field look upon these changes as being at least partially the result of their efforts through public education, special studies and reports, and cooperation and occasionally confrontation with government. Clearly, if the founders of what is now the Canadian Mental Health Association could see these changes, they might be forgiven if they became convinced that their efforts had been effective and very wothwhile.

On the other side of the ledger, unfortunately, we see some of the negative results of all the changes that have occurred. For example, while the number of patients cared for in mental or psychiatric hospitals has declined and the time spent in hospitals much shortened, the number of former patients who are struggling to survive in the community, sometimes against overwhelming difficulties, is discouragingly large. Inpatient care for disturbed young people is seriously lacking. Ambulatory care in clinics is often unsuccessful because of the failure of the patients to keep appointments or of the clinical services to provide supervision and aftercare. Co-ordination of services is still inadequate. The great number of drugs now available have themselves caused disturbing side effects or cannot be adequately monitored while the patients are not under almost continuous medical supervision. The conflicts arising in the civil rights field, as to whether or not a patient should be admitted to hospital or even treated medically against his will or discharged when he is not fully recovered, are constantly emerging and are causing increasing public concern. Psychiatry is being criticized for having too much power, for confining people who should not be confined, and for releasing them when they should not be released. A lively anti-psychiatric mood has developed, unfortunatelty sometimes supported by members of other professional disciplines who are competing for responsible roles in the field of mental health and illness. A discordant note is frequently heard from the many-disciplined mental health orchestra. As Dr. Sydney Smith, the late president of the University of Toronto, said in his welcoming address at the 1954 International Congress on Mental Health in Toronto: "I have, before now, expressed a degree of scepticism about the value of a concerted blast on a miscellany of academic trumpets. Multi-disciplinary thinking should not become muddy-disciplinary thinking."

Has the proportion of Canadians suffering from

identifiable and diagnosable mental illness been reduced in proportion to the total population since 1918? Have the millions spent in mental health research resulted in any definite breakthrough in either treatment or prevention? No one can answer these questions exactly. We have impressions and opinions but few verifiable facts. The best we can say is that, on the whole, things are better now than they used to be. An individual suffering from mental illness today is usually not locked in a foul and dismal cell. Nor is he chained or tied up in some form of restraint. He is usually cared for with kindness and sensitivity. His chances of at least apparent recovery are certainly better than they were fifty years ago.

Can any of these improvements be traced directly to the work of the Canadian Mental Health Association? Probably. While there is no way of proving this, the public education program of the Association over the years seems certainly to have been effective. A great deal is known by the average citizen today about the nature and extent of mental illness and the treatment programs available. True, there is still apprehension and fear when it is encountered personally, and there is still stigma; but the level of public understanding has certainly improved.

It is also true that the various surveys and special studies conducted by the Association on provincial mental health services, including the mental hospitals, beginning with the Manitoba survey in 1918 and reaching a peak with the Tyhurst Report *More for the Mind* in 1963, have had considerable impact on these services. But the estimated extent of mental illness today does not seem to indicate any great improvement. At least eight people in every hundred will suffer from depression requiring treatment during their lifetimes, while one in a hundred will be afflicted by schizophrenia, one of the most persistently chronic of mental illnesses.

If an attempt were made to forecast what is likely to happen in the next fifty years, it would undoubtedly stress the emerging importance of neurophysiology, neurochemistry, neuropharmacology and genetics in the field of psychiatry. Such developments may well bring the treatment of mental illness closer to that available for organic and physical illness and develop a stronger relationship to internal medicine and neurology. There are even those who argue that the present interest in psychotherapy may diminish as more precise medical treatment becomes available. Quite the reverse is likely to happen. As the biological aspects of mental health and illness increase in importance the psycho-social aspects will also expand and the field of psychotherapy will become both more specific in individual treatment and more diverse in its widening concern with social and community factors. Throughout its history much of the effort of the Association has actually been directed to the positive aspects of the problem in an effort to prevent illness and especially to promote good mental health as an indispensable aspect of a fulfilled and productive human life. So, programs of research on such projects as the development and education of young children, parent education and teacher training, mental health in industry, and the management and reduction of stress have characterized the activities of the organization since the early years. Evaluation and assessment of these programs, as in the case of therapeutic programs, are always difficult and to date no substantial proof of their effectiveness has been forthcoming. As in physical hygiene which emphasizes the importance of such things as fresh air, good food and exercise, mental hygiene can stress obvious environmental factors such as the baby's need for tender loving care, social and physical interaction and stimulation. But strictly controlled statistical proof of the effectiveness of these is so far beyond our reach.

Quite apart from the changing scene in mental health, there are a number of reasons why an historical assessment and narrative history of the Canadian Mental Health Association should be undertaken now. The number of people who worked with Dr. C.M. Hincks, the founder and first secretary of the organization, is rapidly diminishing. The author of this present work was his successor as General Director and himself retired in 1971. He is one of only two or three people still living who were employed on staff and worked personally with Dr. Hincks for a number of years. Between them, Hincks and the author, with the sanction of the Board, directed the national association from 1918 to 1971.

Before he died, Hincks wrote an autobiographical manuscript which has proved to be a marvellous source of anecdotal and historical material. Dr. C. Roland, now the Hannah Professor of the History of Medicine at McMaster University, compiled a more formal biography of Dr. Hincks, leaning heavily on his autobiographical notes. Neither manuscript has been published but copies of both these documents are in the CMHA archival collection and have been utilized freely.*

---

*The CMHA Collection is now on permanent loan to the Archives at the Queen Street Mental Health Centre, Toronto.

Apart from these unpublished manuscripts, the author has depended for his material on the archival records of the Association. These include the minutes of meetings of the successive Boards of Directors, of scientific committees and councils, and research and study groups, as well as published reports in professional journals and in books produced by or under the supervision of the Association. In addition, many of the early letters and telegrams which passed between Hincks and his colleagues have been available. These have been freely excerpted and quoted.

The material presented here is organized, more or less, chronologically. The chapters and sections deal with the major program activities, accomplishments, and structural changes in the Association. A list of National Presidents, Scientific Advisors and Staff will be found in appendix A, B, and C. The Presidents and Executive Officers of the Provincial Divisions are listed in Appendix D.

The author, who retired from his post as General Director in 1971, has not been directly involved in the work of the Association for many years. For this reason, much of the final chapter was written as a postscript by George Rohn, who retired as General Director of CMHA in 1987. He, in turn, was generously assisted in this task by Gordon Morwood, Director of Program and Research, and Edward Pennington, currently the General Director.

Discerning readers will appreciate that this book is presented, not as a critical history but as a documentary chronicle of the CMHA; a pioneer organization that has contributed and continues to contribute enormously to the social well-being of Canadians. It is also a tribute to the membership of the CMHA volunteers as well as the staff, who helped to create Canada's humane health and welfare system which is envied all over the world.

The successful completion of a work of this kind depends on the contribution of many willing hands. I am, of course, most grateful for the support provided by the staff of the CMHA, National Office and the Queen Street Mental Health Centre Archives Committee. But most of all I am indebted to my good friends and colleagues Judy Bohnen, John Robert Colombo, Cyril Greenland, Margaret Stanley, Mina Sussman and to Sam Sussman who generously provided editorial assistance.

J.D. Griffin
January 1989, Toronto

I

The Background

1. Origin and Growth of Voluntary Work

There have always been people who have been ready to volunteer their time, effort, and resources to help those in need or those disabled by disease. With reference to those who are mentally disordered, records from earliest colonial times in Canada illustrate the interest and activity of volunteers working in this field. One has only to review the work of the Charon Frères and Madame d'Youville and her Grey Nuns in Montreal during the late 17th and early 18th century to find instances of lay organizations established at least in part for this purpose.[1] By the end of the 18th century and throughout the early 19th century, institutions variously called almshouses, poor houses, houses of industry, etc., were being established in the Maritime provinces as well as in central Canada. The role of volunteer societies organized to assist these institutions is well documented.[2] By the mid-19th century, many prominent physicians and laymen were organizing petitions to the government to urge the development of appropriate asylums for the insane. The names of The Honourable Hugh Bell, mayor of Halifax, Dr. William Rees of Toronto, and Dr. Henry Stabb of Newfoundland may be coupled with that of the crusading Dorothea Dix from New England as instances of people dedicated to this end.[3]

As early as 1898, Dr C.K. Clarke drew attention to a voluntary After Care Society which had been active in England to assist discharged mental patients in their readjustment to community life. This society had been organized by a reverend Mr. Hawkins, of Colney Hatch Asylum in 1879, and was strongly supported by the leading British alienists. Lord Shaftesbury, chairman of the Lunacy Commission, became president.[4] Similar organizations were active in other European countries. Clarke thought that Ontario should have such a society, and so recommended in the section "After-Care of the Insane" in his Annual Report of the Medical Superintendent, Rockwood Asylum, Kingston, Ont., September 30, 1898, pp. 120-1:

> Many of these discharged patients are of unstable nervous type and need protection far more than robust and healthy types. They are frequently without relatives and without money, and when they leave us, necessarily encounter many hardships which they are ill fitted to endure. Lack of employment, shelter, food, clothing, exposure are all encountered; in fact the very conditions necessary to produce a relapse, in which chance of recovery is very much endangered. We are powerless to remedy matters, but a well managed After-Care Association could do wonders. Canada has been criticised for its neglect of this important question, but no doubt the defect will be remedied when attention is drawn to the matter.

No action resulted from Clarke's recommendation,

although public interest in the management and training of feeble-minded children gradually increased. In 1896 the question of custodial care for so-called feeble-minded women was brought before the National Council of Women of Canada by Dr. A.M. Rosebrugh of Hamilton. At the next annual meeting, a Standing Committee was appointed to gather information, with the idea of seeking custodial care for feeble-minded women of child-bearing age. In 1899, after hearing reports of this committee, it was decided that local Councils of Women should petition their respective Provincial Legislatures urging them to make provision for custodial care. As a result of pressure of this kind the Ontario Government in 1906 began an official investigation into the number of feeble-minded women in the province. In 1908 the first Canadian voluntary society for the protection of feeble-minded children was organized in Nova Scotia.[5] By 1913 it had expanded to fifty local branches.[6]

It should be pointed out that this movement seemed largely concerned with placing the mentally retarded in institutions to prevent them from propagating. The leader of this movement in Ontario in 1906-20 was Dr. Helen MacMurchy.[7] In 1912, following a "Great Conference of Cities, Towns, and Municipalities of Ontario," held in Toronto, a Provincial Association for the Care of the Feeble-Minded was organized. In 1914, Dr. Clarke initiated a "Social Service Clinic" at the Toronto General Hospital (TGH) with the help of Dr. C.M. Hincks, Dr. O.C.J. Withrow and two nurses who acted as social workers.[8] With the financial assistance of the Toronto branch of the Association for the Care of the Feeble-Minded, Dr. Clarke became director of the psychological laboratory at the University of Toronto, and intelligence tests became an important diagnostic tool.[9] Also in Toronto, an Advisory Committee of prominent citizens was formed to survey the needs of the mentally retarded and make recommendations to the Mayor and Board of Control of Toronto.[10] This committee urged that: more classes for "backward" children be established in Toronto public schools; a register of all mental defectives be kept by the Medical Officer of Health; and a "Psycho-Educational" clinic for the diagnosis and assistance of all such persons be established.

It is obvious that these recommendations were not new. Some special classes had already been established through Dr. MacMurchy's efforts. Dr. Clarke's clinic at the TGH was already functioning. Nevertheless, a repeated affirmation of the importance of these services helped to bring community, provincial, and even national interest to the level of action. The Honourable Judge Frank Hodgins was appointed by the Ontario government in 1917 to head a Royal Commission to inquire into the methods of dealing with mental defectives. His report was a comprehensive document which again urged the organization of special classes, the establishment of a new hospital training school, and the creation of a wide range of industrial and agricultural training programs designed to provide mentally retarded persons with useful skills.[11]

Meanwhile, a number of related events took place that before long had important effects on Canada. In 1908, Clifford Whittingham Beers published his famous book *A Mind that Found Itself*.[12] The next year he organized first the Connecticut Society for Mental Hygiene and then the National Committee for Mental Hygiene Inc. Beers credited the use of the term "mental hygiene" to a suggestion made by Adolf Meyer, Professor of Psychiatry at

John's Hopkins, but the term was by no means new even in North America. It first appeared in the literature in 1843 in a book written by Dr. W.C. Sweetser of the University of Vermont. His book was called *Mental Hygiene: or an Examination of the Intellect and Passions Designed to Illustrate their influence on Health and the Duration of Life.* A long essay, titled "Mental Hygiene" written by Dr. George Cook of Brigham Hall, Canandaigua, N.Y., was published in 1859[13] and a book by Dr. Isaac Ray with the same title appeared in 1863.[14] Both these works stressed the importance of heredity and the baneful effect on the progeny in marriages between close relatives and both authors warned of the dangers of too much study and lack of proper rest during the formative years.

Dr. Joseph Workman of Toronto, never reluctant to discuss any issue, had a lot to say about mental hygiene. He strongly deprecated the system of education advocated at that time, since it tended to place children in "a forced draft of intellectual development in order to become infant prodigies." He observed that infant prodigies often became adult fools. He felt that chidren should not be sent to school until they reached the age of seven years.[15]

The Canadian Medical Association (CMA) appointed a Committee on Mental Hygiene with Dr. Helen MacMurchy as chairman and Dr. E.H. Young as secretary. These two met once in Kingston in 1914, and while unable to attend the CMA convention that year, they asked that the Committee be continued for another year so that in 1915 "we might present a comprehensive resumé of the progress made in mental hygiene in this and other countries, and we hope also to be prepared to make suggestions for further progress in the conservation of mental health in Canada."[16] This resumé never was presented as the 1915 meeting of the CMA was cancelled. Its president and secretary were in the army overseas.

2. Clarence M. Hincks and Clifford W. Beers

The first national meeting of state societies for mental hygiene in the United States was held in 1914 in Baltimore and was reported at length by Dr. E.H. Young.[17] In spite of the exigencies of war in Europe, an atmosphere of heady excitement about the importance of mental hygiene was developing, especially in Toronto. As Dr. Hincks described this period:

> After working with Dr. Clarke in the outpatient clinic for two or three years, I became restless and impatient. I felt the knowledge about mental illness and mental deficiency which we had acquired ought to be put to use somehow across Canada. I knew that many of our asylums were inadequate and our immigration screening was poor. I was aware that we were not doing what should be done to help rehabilitate the psychiatric casualties among our soldiers. No one was doing anything about prevention.[18]

Late in 1917, Hincks discussed his ideas with Clarke. He found ready agreement with the need for improving psychiatric services across the country, but neither knew how to go about it. They agreed that as a first step Hincks should discuss the idea with some of the leading medical, psychiatric, and neurological scientists in the United States, probably in New York. Hincks did this but found no one who would offer much help. Then, almost by accident, he was introduced to Clifford W. Beers. Hincks had forgotten that four years previously he had referred to Beers and his work in a column written for the *Toronto Star* while he was covering an International Conference on School Hygiene in Buffalo.[19] was not likely ever to forget him again. Beers gave

Hincks a copy of his book *A Mind that Found Itself* and told him to return it next morning after he had read it. Dr. Hincks was not a fast reader; however, he stayed up most of the night in order to get the gist of it. Beers in his book gives a graphic account of his own mental illness and the treatment he received, some of it rather abusive and even cruel. With the encouragement and support of William James, Professor of Psychology at Harvard, this book was published in 1908. It proved to have a significant influence in launching the mental hygiene movement and it still lives as a classic.

The next day Hincks and Beers spent hours together planning how to extend the mental hygiene movement into Canada. They were compatible in an unusual way. They both had a contagious enthusiasm which at times became excited exuberance. Hincks had more drive and sustained energy, while Beers was more cautious, was more experienced in organizing work, and had a much bigger ego. Both were cyclothymic and subject to occasional periods of fatigue, anxiety, depression, and apathy. As long as they were not depressed at the same time, they made an excellent team. The flow of correspondence and telegrams between them during the next year reflected their excitement about their project. On occasion several letters and a telegram would arrive from Beers dated the same day, and each was answered with equal enthusiam. Beers promised to come to Canada to help Hincks organize a Canadian mental hygiene committee. He wanted Hincks to join him in creating a world-wide mental hygiene movement and thought that a Canadian committee would be an excellent first step.[20]

3. Preliminary Meetings and Formal Organization

Hincks wasted no time. He began immediately to list friends and interested professional people who might agree to become members of his committee. He felt he should recruit support among the medical profession first, and since he knew he could count on reasonable support from the University of Toronto because of the backing of C.K. Clarke, Dean of Medicine and Professor of Psychiatry, he decided to visit McGill University in Montreal first. He had one powerfull ally at McGill in Lieutenant Colonel Colin Russel who was Professor of Neurology and consultant to the Canadian Army Medical Corps. Through him he met Sir William Peterson, the principal at McGill, who in turn arranged for Hincks to address the Medical Faculty. His persuasiveness and sincerity won unanimous approval.

Back in Toronto he began to organize what became a series of "drawing-room meetings." These were afternoon teas hosted by socially prominent women, each of whom invited about twenty of her wealthy and influential friends. His plan was to try to have Beers present as a special guest. Usually Clarke would give or lend copies of Beers' book to those who showed special interest. He had no trouble in recruiting an impressive list of potential members and donors. The first of these meetings was held on February 26, 1918, at the home of Mrs. D.A. Dunlap in Toronto. In a way this was where the organization began.

A report in The *Globe* the following day recorded the event under the heading "$20,000 SECURED FOR INSTITUTE: CANADIAN NATIONAL COMMITTEE FOR MENTAL HYGIENE STARTED IN MRS. DUNLAP'S HOME."

"I never saw people so enjoy being asked for money" was the comment of one of the small group who gathered in Mrs. D.A. Dunlap's hospitable home on Highland Avenue yesterday afternoon to hear Mr. Clifford W. Beers of New York and to discuss the organization of a Canadian National Committee for Mental Hygiene. Probably that enjoyment was largely due to the fact that Mr. Beers manifestly and avowedly enjoyed it himself. In any case the mutual enjoyment was so very effective that before Mrs. Dunlap's guests had gone approximately $20,000 had been pledged towards guaranteeing the first three years work of a Canadian National Committee for Mental Hygiene. And this is just the beginning in Toronto of what is to be a national movement and one to which large contributions will doubtless still be made, both in Toronto and other parts of the Dominion.

National Committee Formed

Dr. C.K. Clarke presided at the meeting and Dr. C.M. Hincks acted as secretary. Dr. Clarke spoke briefly on the need of an organization for mental hygiene in Canada and then called upon Mr. Beers who told this most responsive audience the wonderful story of his mental breakdown, his experiences during that time, his recovery, and the work of prevention and help for others which he undertook as a result.

Dr. E.A. Bott and Major J.G. Fitzgerald spoke of the need of a similar work in Canada and it was moved by Colonel Colin Russel of Montreal and seconded by Dr. Peter Bryce, Medical Director of the Department of Immigration at Ottawa:

"Whereas the National Committee for Mental Hygiene, founded in 1909 in the United States, has convincingly demonstrated the value of and need for similar organizations in all enlightened countries, and whereas many of the problems that are being studied and solved by the National Committee in the United States likewise require prompt attention and study in Canada such, for instance, as the problems of mental health, nervous and mental disorders, mental deficiency, epilepsy, inebriety, and the mental factors involved in crime, prostitution, pauperism, immigration and the like and,

Whereas the National Committee for Mental Hygiene in the United States has been able to perform important duties in connection with the war, be it therefore

Resolved that it is the sense of this meeting that an organization to be known as the Canadian National Committee for Mental Hygiene and having purposes similar to those of the National Committee for Mental Hygiene of the United States be organized without delay."

An organizing committee was formed on the resolution of Mrs. A.M. Huestis, seconded by Professor Sandiford, to arrange the necessary details with regard to the organization.

A Representative Gathering
Dr. Helen MacMurchy moved a very hearty vote of thanks to Mrs. Dunlap for giving her home for the meeting and her enthusiastic support to the movement, expressing at the same time the gratitude of all to Mr. Beers for coming to Canada to help in the organization. Dr. C.J.O Hastings "in a very happy" speech, seconded the motion.

Among the others present, many of whom expressed their interest in the movement in a very practical way, were: Mrs. P.D. Crerar of Hamilton, Mrs. Adam Ballantyne, Mrs. George Decker, Mr. and Mrs. W.B. Meikle, Mrs. Pepler, Miss Walker, Major and Mrs. Fitzgerald, Mrs. W.B. Hendry, Mrs. Campbell Meyers, Mrs. Foster, Mrs. Sidney Small, Mr. Dunlap, Mr. Wills of Hamilton, Sir Robert Falconer, Mrs. H.D. Warren, Dr. E.J. Pratt, Mr. W.D. Gwynne, Dr. Horace L. Brittain, Dr. Goldwin Howland, Dr. O.C.J. Withrow and Dr. Gordon Bates.

The new Canadian organization is the first national committee to be formed outside the United States and it is hoped that it may be the beginning of an international movement.

In a special survey and critical review of the Canadian National Committee completed in 1932 for the Canadian Medical Association by Dr. J.G. Fitzgerald, University of Toronto, and Dr. Grant Fleming, McGill University[21], a short historical note recorded the purposes and objectives of the organization as tentatively described at the meeting in Mrs. Dunlap's home. These included the following:

1. War work
   (a) Psychiatric examination of recruits.
   (b) Adequate care of returned soldiers suffering from mental disabilities.
2. Mental examination of immigrants (post-war) to ensure a better selection of newcomers.
3. Adequate facilities for the diagnosis and treatment of cases of mental disease.
4. Adequate care of the mentally deficient.
5. Prevention of mental disease and deficiency.

The Dunlap meeting approved the proposed program and the chairman was empowered to appoint an organizing committee. The committee was formed, the initial meeting to be held in Ottawa on April 26th, 1918.

Although originally conceived as informal meetings to gain interest and moral support, Hincks found these drawing-room gatherings useful fund-raising events. Lady Eaton, an old friend of Dr. Hincks, recalled one of these early gatherings.

> He telephoned me and asked me to help him with one of these meetings. At this one Dr. Hincks was the speaker. Mrs. H.D. Warren was also going to be there and I knew that she only believed in people who had something important to give; I agreed. After Dr. Hincks finished speaking he said, "Well, that's it." Mrs. Warren got up and said, "But Dr. Hincks, you can't leave it at that. Aren't you

going to ask for subscriptions?" And he said, "No, I hadn't thought of it." So Mrs. Warren said she would subscribe so much and then looked at me. "Lady Eaton, how about you," and I said, "I'll do the same." $10,000 was pledged at that meeting![22]

Hincks decided that it was time to organize a Board of Directors. With the help of Sir William Peterson, he was able to arrange an interview with the Governor General, the Duke of Devonshire, at Rideau Hall. This must have been a somewhat unusual interview. In Hincks' words:

The Duke's hospitality and courtesy were overpowering . . . He opened the conversation with "I know you are a doctor, but please do not use technical medical language because I am afraid I would not understand you. You know I am a farmer." And so, in very simple language, I told him that the problem of mental disorders was enormous, affecting in one way or another practically every home in Canada; that our arrangements for diagnosis and treatment were grossly inadequate; that we were admitting recruits into the Canadian army who, because of low mentality and emotional instability, could never become effective soldiers; that we were placing many mental patients in jails, even although they had committed no offence against society, because of shortage of hospital beds; that the control of this vast problem needed the co-operation of the public but the public was apathetic or frightened of mental disabilities and did nothing to forward progress; that the medical profession shied away from the whole problem; and so on. I also told the Governor General that the Faculty of Medicine, McGill University, agreed with me that we needed a great national organization to pioneer the way for progress. He asked me what I wanted him to do and I replied that we would appreciate his interest and sponsorship in developing such a national organization. The Governor General replied, "All right, I will be pleased to give my patronage when your board requests me to do so." "But," I said, "we have no board." The Duke looked puzzled and said, "You want my patronage for something that does not exist?" I replied that that was exactly what we wanted. He asked, "Why?" I said that a national organization in our field could not possibly succeed unless we had a board composed of top leaders in Canada - men who were known to all Canadians and who were respected by them. I said that our field was a hush-hush one and that some Canadians might think we were crack-pots or do-gooders unless our board was composed of hard headed businessmen who would not be taken in by anything that could be considered shaky or phony. I told His Excellency that any board I could assemble on my own would be second or third rate and quite useless for our purposes. I also explained that if he would endorse us now, I would use his name to help assemble the strongest board in Canada - one capable of running the Canadian Pacific Railway or the Bank of Montreal. The Govenor General thought a minute and said, "You win. I will extend my patronage now even although I am acting contrary to all precedents," and then he added, "My wife will help you also."[23]

Hardly pausing for breath, Hincks tore back to Montreal and again with the help of Sir William Peterson began building his first Board of Directors. Of the twenty leading business and professional people contacted, eighteen agreed to act. Among these were Lord Shaughnessy, President of the CPR; Richard B. Angus, Montreal financier and philanthropist; Dr. C.F. Martin, Professor of Medicine, McGill University; Sir Vincent Meredith, President, Bank of Montreal; and F.W. Molson, President of Molson's Brewery. Each agreed to pledge $1,000 a year for three years toward the expenses of the new organization. Those people he could not see received letters which were an interesting combination of flattery, reassurance, and perhaps even some guile. A letter written on April 10, 1918, to Sir Edmund Osler requesting his support is typical. It includes the following paragraph:

> With regard to finance I might say that one hundred thousand dollars will carry the Committee for four years. In asking you to become a member we are not appealing primarily for funds, but we want you principally for the moral support you can give the enterprise. At a later date, if the budget demands it, we might, however, present to you our needs. As a matter of fact, I feel that the financing of our Committee is the least serious of all our difficulties, because to date we have received money without making any urgent appeal.

It was successful!

Other drawingroom meetings with Beers and Hincks were planned in homes of friends in Quebec City, Montreal, and Ottawa. Beers was very impressed not only with Hincks' natural enthusiasm but with the fund-raising potential of these drawingroom meetings. He decided to organize similar meetings to be hosted by wealthy ladies in the eastern United States. These at first were not as successful as the Canadian tea parties, and Hincks had to keep encouraging Beers to keep up his efforts.

Finally the organization meeting was held in Ottawa on April 26, 1918. The Canadian National Committee for Mental Hygiene (CNCMH) was formally organized.*A provisional constitution was adopted. Dr. C.F. Martin, Professor of Medicine at McGill University, was elected President. Dr. C.K. Clarke was appointed Medical Director and Dr. C.M. Hincks, Associate Medical Director and Secretary.

---

*The organization applied for and received its legal federal charter in December 1926 (see p.54

Within a few days of the Ottawa meeting, Beers began to worry about the constitution and by-laws. Dr. Peter Bryce, a highly respected civil servant, was already suggesting changes from the draft prepared by Beers. Beers in his letter of May 7, 1918, was beginning to show signs of ego sensitivity and irritation with anyone wishing to modify his plans and patterns for a world-wide network of National Committees, all with the same (or similar) constitutions. His assumption of proprietorship in thanking Bryce for "arranging the Ottawa meeting" is apparent. It is almost as if the Canadian Committee was to be a branch of the U.S. National Committee. His written caution to Dr. Hincks on Hincks' copy of the letter to Dr. Bryce is interesting. It reads: "Put the lid on Dr. Bryce and Prof. Small of Ottawa, if they suggest too many changes in the By-Laws."

In a somewhat similar vein, Dr. Hincks suggested that he was thinking of approaching the Rockefeller Foundation for a special grant to finance a project related to juvenile delinquency in Montreal. Beers at once cautioned against it. His stated reasons were related to the absence from the country of two key persons, Dr. Thomas Salmon, the Medical Director of the National Committee, and Dr. Edwin R. Embree, secretary of the Rockefeller Foundation. Dr. Salmon had distinguished himself in organizing psychiatric services for the United States Army in France and was highly regarded by the Rockefeller organization. Hincks immediately gave up any idea of approaching the foundation at this time. Perhaps he gave up too early, for one gets the impression that Beers may have been protecting American sources of funds for his own committee.

There were good reasons why Hincks wanted a tangible project started in Montreal. The Montreal group of sponsors and board members were beginning to be restive about the fact that the CNCMH staff and program activists all seemed to be in Toronto. A further indication of their concern was their reluctance to approve any remuneration for Dr. Clarke who was beginning to spend most of his time on Committee affairs.

In the fall the Committee established itself in an office across the road from the Toronto General Hospital at 143 College Street, consisting of four rooms on the second floor. In addition to Clarke and Hincks, the staff comprised Miss Marjorie Keyes and two secretaries, Anne Abbott and Doris Secord. Miss Keyes, a graduate nurse from the TGH, had been associated with Dr. Clarke and Dr. Hincks in the Out-Patient Psychiatric Clinic. During the summer of 1918, arrangements were made to enable her to attend Smith College for training in psychiatric work. The CNCMH was then ready for action.

II

The First
Projects 1918-23

1. The Manitoba Survey

Very soon after the CNCMH was organized, Lieutenant Colonel Colin Russel helped provide an opportunity for it to undertake an important project. He was consultant neurologist to the Department of Soldiers' Civil Re-Establishment and to the Army Medical Corps and had visited many of the provincial mental hospitals which were caring for soldier patients. He was distressed with conditions in some of these hospitals and was particulary critical of those in Manitoba.

The Manitoba Government had established a special Public Welfare Commission in October, 1917, to review all the charitable institutions in the province, including the jails and hospitals. The Commission had already become concerned about the mental hospitals, and under pressure from Colonel Russel agreed to seek the help of the newly-formed National Committee. In the late summer of 1918 a letter from the Commission's secretary, A.P. Paget, requesting that this survey be carried out, was sent to Colonel Russel. The survey was to have reference not only to the mental hospitals but also to all institutions presently caring for the mentally disordered or defective, including jails, schools, special homes, and juvenile courts. All legislation pertaining to these institutions would also be reviewed.

The newly-constituted staff of the National Committee was excited by the prospect of such an important assignment. However, it was impossible for Dr. Clarke to take part in the work until after the middle of October because of previous commitments. Since neither Dr. Hincks nor Miss Keyes had had experience or training in mental hospital work, the first thought was to seek help from the American National Committee. Dr. William H. Russell, a very respected neuro-psychiatrist, chairman of its executive committee, indicated he would be willing to go to Manitoba in order to help but could not be available until later in the fall. In the end it was decided that Hincks and Miss Keyes would go alone to make a preliminary survey. Dr. Clarke, the most experienced and knowledgeable psychiatrist in Canada at that time, would join them later. This plan enabled Hincks and Keyes to gain valuable experience and make observations on their own which could be carefully checked later by Dr. Clarke.

They wasted no more time and arrived in Winnipeg on September 30, 1918. Judging by the number of institutions visited, they completed an astonishing amount of work within a matter of days. They visited the Salvation Army Industrial Home, the Juvenile Court, several public schools, and the Home for Incurables in Portage la Prairie and were so shocked by what they found that they immediately returned to Winnipeg to consult with government representatives. A wire was sent to Dr. C.K. Clarke in Toronto urging him to join them as soon as possible. While awaiting Clarke's arrival, they met the Premier, Mr. Norris, his Cabinet, and the members of the Public Welfare Commission. Dr. Hincks recalled that the group was deeply concerned about the conditions being discovered by the National Committee and promised full co-operation and remedial action.

The Committee prepared a confidential report on its findings which was submitted to the government and the Public Welfare Commission. The latter body published most of this report in its Second Interim Report. However, its version lacks much of the hard-hitting, critical, and colourful quality of the original. The following extracts are from the original report.

> The most painful and distressing survey undertaken while we were in Manitoba was at the so-called Home for Incurables at Portage la Prairie. Two visits were made, the first on October 8, 1918, the second on October 15, 1918, as we did not wish to labour under any misapprehension in regard to what was seen there. The name, Home for Incurables, is misleading, and the institution has become a recuperation house for every kind of ailment, - as one of our party expressed it, "from eczema to dementia." Apparently any family in Manitoba which had a troublesome member, either old or young, simply passed the problem on to the Home for Incurables, until this institution possessed an unhappy conglomeration of idiots, imbeciles, epileptics, insane, seniles, and mentally normal people suffering from incurable diseases. Of course, this state of affairs is the outcome of the want of proper institutions in the province to care for the different classes represented, but it is difficult to realize the system of inspection which allowed such a condition of affairs to develop. That insane people should be housed in this institution is astonishing, as it is devoid of

any equipment for caring for cases of insanity. The result has been tragic in the extreme.[1]

Dr. Hincks reported further that, while the Superintendent of the Home was a good housekeeper, he was totally untrained and inexperienced in modern psychiatric management. A physician who visited the Home daily also lacked special training and merely attempted to care for the physical ailments of the inmates. When the Home was opened in 1890 it was not intended for the insane. However, by 1918, of the 335 inmates, 102 were classified as feeble-minded, imbecile, or idiot. Absolutely no activity or occupation was provided. The patients simply vegetated. There was serious overcrowding by at least one-third. One room, in area eighteen feet by eight feet, contained sixteen beds or bunks. The ventilation was execrable throughout. Physical restraint and seclusion were commonly used. There were six patients with hands confined in canvas "muffs," presumably to prevent violence against themselves or others. The report finally observed: "These patients would never have reached the level to which they had sunk had they been cared for intelligently in the early stages of their disease." Hincks described one patient in seclusion who deeply affected him.

> At the end of a long dark ward a cupboard was found containing a naked woman with deathly pale skin. There was no furniture, no bed, not even a mattress. The woman had a small piece of shawl which she placed over her eyes when the door was opened. Apparently she was unaccustomed to light. When the Superintendent was asked how long this woman had been left in the cupboard, he replied, "two years." Hincks asked how often she had been permitted out during that period. "Once, and then only for ten minutes in a cage. She was restless, so we returned her

to the cupboard."[2]

Hincks and Miss Keyes followed their visit to the Home by visits to the jails. They had discovered that all patients admitted to mental institutions had to be committed by a magistrate. For many this meant that they had to be confined in a jail pending a court session. Later they were transported to the "appropriate" institution. Apart from the indignity of a sick disabled person being sent to jail, the treatment accorded the patient there exposed him or her to additional hazards. If the patient was overactive or aggressive, he was often brutally handled. "Many patients arrived at the institution in a battered and bruised condition. Sometimes the transfer was made with the patient chained or fastened to a metal grill for easy handling!" Voluntary admission to mental hospital was not possible.

Hincks and the committee rarely blamed individual staff persons responsible for these conditions. While very critical of the inadequacies and abuses, the report concluded: "Much as we deprecate the conditions as found, we realize that it is scarcely fair to censure the officials who have a task imposed on them which they are not trained to undertake. They simply do their best to meet an awkward situation."[3]

A similar attitude characterized the comments written after inspecting the Brandon Hospital for the Insane. Hincks was keenly aware of deficiencies in this asylum. But he was quick to point out that the Medical Superintendent, J.B. Chambers, M.D., was the only physician on staff caring for seven hundred patients, and simply could not be expected to do much more than attend to the innumerable demands of administration.

I will never forget the shock I received when we started our study at the Brandon Asylum. There were 700 patients with only one physician, who was the superintendent. Practically all his time was spent supervising the asylum farm and in filling in death certificates. He had no time for the treatment of patients. There was not one trained nurse in the establishment. The male attendants were the roughest looking group of men I had ever seen. . . Because of the number of black eyes among the patients, it was evident that these attendants used strong-arm methods of control. Over many of the beds there had been placed heavy iron grating giving the patients underneath the appearance of caged wild animals. Patients sat in complete idleness on long hard wooden benches, many of them in physical restraint, staring vacantly into space, dejected, waiting for death to give them release. Restless patients were placed in solitary confinement in small desolate rooms.[4]

The Selkirk Hospital for the Insane, was the last institution to be inspected by the committee and was the oldest hospital of its kind in the province. It had been partially completed in 1886 and since then several additions had been made. The physical facilities compared favourably with those at Brandon. However, as at Brandon, the single physician in charge was required to care for nearly four hundred patients and to supervise all administration. Attendants, (thirty-four male and twenty-five female), acted as custodians. There were no trained nurses. No attempt was made to keep accurate medical records, and there were no laboratory or research facilities. The committee concluded: "Selkirk is on the whole admirably managed as a custodial institution, but totally unfitted to meet the demands of a modern hospital for the insane. The management was to be heartily congratulated on having achieved such excellent results with such meagre equipment and resources."[5] The confidential report ended with recommendations for action which were included in the report of the Public Welfare Commission. Its published recommendations indicated the willingness of the Commission to agree with the findings of the National Committee. The first recommendation set the stage for those to follow: "Hospitals for the Insane should be regarded as being on the same plane as other hospitals and no longer as mere custodial institutions. . ." Yet no series of recommendations is worth the paper it is written on unless some action follows. The first session of the legislature of Manitoba after the report was received was held January 23, 1919. The Speech from the Throne stated that:

> The work of the Public Welfare Commission, its survey and special classification of mental diseases and the near completion of the Psychopathic Institute which, as part of the Winnipeg General Hospital, would introduce into the new system of treatment the most humane and scientific methods anywhere in vogue and prevent mental cases from passing through the gaols as in the past.[6]

Perhaps it is significant that the National Committee is not mentioned. Hincks always held that so long as the Committee was making surveys, the policy should be to keep reports confidential and to provide critical information only to the government and responsible officials. He felt the organization should keep in the background as far as possible and not claim special recognition. By this close co-operation, Hincks felt that the government would obtain full credit for any reforms undertaken and the working relationship with the Committee would be enhanced. This policy changed somewhat since that time, but a desire to work *with* rather than against government has continued.

One very important recommendation requiring new legislation was the elimination of the archaic system of commitment through the jails by magistrates. Later in January, 1919, R.S. Thorton, Minister of Education and a physician, sponsored a bill which provided for the admission of patients directly to psychopathic and mental hospitals without a magistrate's commitment. The bill also changed the name of Brandon and Selkirk Hospitals for the Insane to Hospitals for Mental Diseases, provided for voluntary commitment, and allowed the Lieutenant-Governor-in-Council to make rules and regulations for the management and care of patients in these institutions. Physical abuse of patients was prohibited. The bill was passed and became the Mental Diseases Act of 1919.[7]

The Government of Manitoba finally gave full credit to the National Committee. On March 14, 1919, The Honourable J.W. Armstrong, Provincial Secretary, sent the following telegram to Dr. Hincks:

> You will be pleased to know that the Manitoba Legislature today passed enabling legislation to carry out recommendations embodied in the report of your Committee to the Public Welfare Commission of Manitoba. The Canadian National Committee for Mental Hygiene has rendered our government valuable service, and we wish you and your Committee all success in its splendid national work.[8]

2. Other Provincial Surveys

As a result of the Manitoba survey and that province's quick response in implementing the recommendations, other provinces became interested in having similar surveys. The fact that the Department of Soldiers' Civil Re-establishment in Ottawa was bringing increasing pressure on the provinces to provide improved treatment for the psychiatric casualties among returned soldiers must also have helped. During the next four years, requests for surveys were received from British Columbia, New Brunswick, Nova Scotia, Prince Edward Island, Alberta, and Saskatchewan. As in Manitoba, these surveys included all institutions, facilities, and agencies concerned with mental disorders. The work was time-consuming and kept Dr. Hincks and Miss Keyes very busy travelling and visiting from coast to coast. Dr. Clarke was always available as an adviser and consultant but left most of the spade work to Hincks and Keyes.

The need for such surveys was shown by the conditions revealed and the confidential and occasionally public reports made to the governments concerned. It seems incredible that conditions reported during special investigations made some fifty years previously were commonly encountered again. As an example, a Grand Jury visited the Prince Edward Island asylum in 1874 and reported that:

> They find it difficult to ask your Lordship to believe that an institution, so conducted, would be allowed exist in a civilized community. In a cell below the ground, about six feet by seven feet, they found a young women, entirely naked, beneath some broken, dirty straw. The stench was unbearable. There were pools of urine on the floor, evidently the accumulation of many days, as there were gallons of it. The superintendent of the institution was apparently "an ordinary labourer" and the Jury concluded that "the whole Asylum is one state of filth."[9]

Similarly, in an investigation into the management of the Hospital for the Insane at Darmouth (Mount Hope), Nova Scotia, in 1872, an attendant told the following story:

A patient named Graham was in a dark room (solitary confinement) while I was at the Hospital. It was in the winter time. The glass was broken and the rain came in and wet the floor. Graham was lying on the floor on a mattress. The room was in a very dirty condition. There was straw on the floor and human excrements. I saw the snow melt on the floor. We put food over the door sometimes. The doctor would occasionally enquire how he was. . . He never went to see him. A man put in the dark room was entirely neglected. Graham was subject to fits; he might have died without assistance during the night; he was left entirely to his own resources after locking him up. Graham was a powerful, muscular man. It was the practice of the attendants to give as little food as possible to patients in that state to reduce their strength; just enough food to sustain them. The doctors never enquired into the quantity of food given them. Graham was in the dark room from one to three weeks. The room was bitterly cold; it was hardly fit for a dog; it was not fit for a human being.[10]

Fifty years later conditions were but little improved. Dr. Hincks, in recalling the mental hospital surveys, stated:

We discovered many things that shocked us. In the asylum in Saint John, New Brunswick, for example, we found on the top floor a group of patients who were put to bed in coffin-like boxes, with hay in the bottom and slats on the top and who were locked in these boxes at night. Two of these boxes were left unlocked for patients who were trusties and who were given the job of dealing with noisy patients. They accomplished their task through a revolting procedure by urinating through the slat openings on the faces of noisy patients. Miss Keyes and I felt that no one would believe our story about the coffin-like boxes; so we asked to have one shipped to our national office.[11]

★ ★ ★

In Edmonton, Alberta, we saw the way they looked after

low-grade, mentally defective children. They rolled each child in a long strip of cotton with arms and legs bound and placed these children on shelves for the night. It apparently never occured to the authorities to use beds.

★ ★ ★

In Halifax, Nova Scotia, we saw a scantily-clothed man in a small unheated room who was kept there throughout the cold damp weather. When we remonstrated with the authorities, we were told that the insane man did not feel the cold. Of course, this was utter nonsense.[12]

There were, however, many facilities and institutions throughout Canada inspected by Hincks and Keyes which were doing splendid work and were managed in exemplary fashion. Frequently described with praise and enthusiasm was the Maritime Home for Girls situated at Truro, Nova Scotia, and directed by Miss Strothard. This residential school received delinquent girls from the three maritime provinces and was one of few successful facilities operated jointly by the provinces. With judicious use of academic training, domestic science, occupational activity and sports, and a personality which encouraged the girls to develop a trusting and warm affection for her, Miss Strothard accomplished wonders.

Another excellent example was the occupational therapy program at the North Battleford Provincial Hospital in Saskatchewan. This was largely the work of the matron, Miss Hazel Jaques, who in a sense "attached a lot of the patients to her staff - people with skills in many lines of work.[13] The products and the craft work of Battleford patients became famous throughout the province.

The work of visiting provincial institutions and of consulting almost annually with the government ministries and officials concerned continued for many years. Hincks used to remark that Miss Keyes had spent more time in mental hospitals and jails than any other woman in Canada!

3. War Work

It was a time of burgeoning interest and concern in psychological medicine. One of the major factors contributing to this interest was the realization that thousands of soldiers were being invalided home from overseas with psychiatric disorders of all kinds. At first those needing further hospital care were sent to their home provinces to be cared for in provincial mental hospitals. In January, 1917, the Ontario Mental Hospital at Cobourg was taken over by the Dominion government as a military psychiatric hospital. Many soldiers either from overseas or from Canadian bases were referred for diagnosis and treatment to the Psychiatric Clinic at the Toronto General Hospital or to the newly established Department of Soldiers' Civil Re-establishment (DSCR) in Ottawa.

It became obvious to Dr. Clarke and Colonel Russel that many of the soldiers being cared for in the provincial institutions were not receiving adequate treatment. The DSCR appointed Dr. C.B. Farrar as a full-time psychiatrist and arranged for his commission as a Captain (later Major). Farrar and Clarke, assisted by Miss Keyes, conducted a quick inspection trip of ten provincial hospitals in the western provinces to examine all the soldier patients.*

---

*Dr. Farrar recalled later that when they were in Winnipeg "word reached us that Dr. Clarke would not be permitted to visit any of the Ontario hospitals. In his home province which he had served so faithfully and so long and with such splended results he was persona non grata as far as the government of the day was concerned."[14]

The results of this preliminary survey were finally published in 1920. Undoubtedly the problem of "shell shock" and other neuropsychiatric disorders affecting so many apparently able-bodied men helped pave the way for the work of the National Committee, particularly the detailed institutional surveys carried out by the Committee's staff on the invitation of the provincial governments. It also opened the door for a continuing co-operative program with the DSCR and the Canadian Army Medical Corps. Dr. Clarke and Dr. Farrar noted in their study of one thousand psychiatric cases in the Canadian Army, "The war has rendered a service in forcing upon the attention of psychiatrists and neurologists the fact that the number of mental weaklings in every community is by no means negligible."[15]

The National Committee from the very beginning was deeply concerned about the role it might play in other aspects of military hygiene. At a meeting of the Executive Committee on September 17, 1918, it was decided to seek an interview with Major General Fotheringham, the Director General of Medical Services in Ottawa, urging him to have the Medical Services "employ trained psychiatrists to examine drafted men, in order that mental and nervous misfits should be eliminated; make a closer comparison of data between the Neuro-psychiatric Department of the Surgeon Generals' office at Washington and the Canadian Army Medical Corps; and ensure that attention should be directed to the results obtained in the American army by means of psychological examination."

The exercise was sucessful. General Fotheringham agreed to allow a month-long demonstration by two psychiatric social workers, one in Toronto and one in Montreal. They were to assist the medical boards by making home visits and investigating the backgrounds of psychiatric cases about to be discharged from the army. The procedure was found to be so obviously valuable that a two-month training course in psychiatric social work was organized by the National Committee at the University of Toronto. About forty nurses registered for this course, most of them from the DSCR. This was the beginning of the mental hygiene emphasis in the training of public health nurses and social workers in Canada, work subsequently assumed by universities.*

4. Immigration

Dr. Clarke had long advocated improving the psychiatric screening of immigrants. Many of his public lectures and official reports emphasized this fact. It was logical, therefore, that the National Committee should engage itself in this activity from the start.:

> The National Committee, together with other organizations, was alive to the fundamental importance of the proper examination of immigrants in order to ensure a better selection of newcomers, and to prevent Canada from being a dumping-ground for defectives and degenerates from other countries. The results of an inadequate system of medical examination - physical, but particularly mental - were well known to all hospital, health, social and other workers.
>
> The National Committee, shortly after its organization, arranged with Professor W.G. Smith to make a study of the problem of immigration. This was published in May, 1920, under the title of *A study in Canadian Immigration.*

---

*Unfortunately this experience with neuro-psychiatric casualties in the armed forces was ignored or forgotten by the medical services in the period between the wars and had to be painfully re-learned in 1940-41.

It was decided that the staff of the National Committee should gather first-hand information as to the existing system of examination of immigrants. This was done. There followed, in 1920, a request from the Dominion Government that the National Committee arrange for the psychiatric training of three of their immigration medical inspectors. It was also arranged that one of the officials of the National Committee be lent for four months to the immigration medical services at the port of Quebec, where he demonstrated methods for the mental examination of immigrants.[16]

5. Work in the Schools

Reflecting the early work of Dr. Hincks in the public schools of Toronto and the influence of Dr. Helen MacMurchy, the Committee began immediately to press for surveys of school children. The surveys would assess the extent of mental retardation and other psychiatric disorders and to provide support for the establishment of auxiliary classes for the special education of such children.

In September, 1919, the City Council of Toronto, on the recommendation of its Medical Officer of Health, Dr. C.J.O. Hastings, appointed Dr. Clarke's daughter, Miss Emma De V. Clarke, "to take charge of the mental hygiene work of the Department." She had worked with her father and Dr. Hincks at the TGH Psychiatric Clinic before going overseas with a military hospital. The next month Council appointed Dr. Eric Clarke, C.K. Clarke's son, who also had been overseas on military duty, to take charge of the psychiatric work in the schools. In August, 1920, Dr. Hastings reported that during the past school year "our psychiatrist has examined school children in 38 schools in the poorer sections of the city. 538 (1.6% of the children) were mentally defective."[17] Thus began the first Canadian psychiatric service for school children provided by a local Department of Health. It was hoped that it would become a truly preventive mental hygiene service. It was formally organized as a Division of Mental Hygiene in 1927.

In the winter of 1920-1, a young graduate student Dr. E.J. Pratt, who was later to be recognized as a notable professor of English and a poet, began one of the first research projects sponsored by the Committee. He conducted a survey of one school where every child was examined, both physically and psychologically.[18] [19] Dr. Pratt remained a close personal friend of Hincks for the rest of his life. Following this, careful surveys of school children were made in many other Ontario cities. Altogether some 1669 children were tested by means of a modified Binet-Simon Test of Intelligence. These children were referred for examination by their teachers because they were suspected of being retarded or feeble-minded. Of these, 1311 were found to be retarded and suitable for special education in auxiliary or opportunity classes. In some instances, institutional care seemed advisable.[20] In Montreal a survey was made of the children in the Protestant schools by Dr. A.G. Morphy and Professor William Tait.[21]

6. Occupational Therapy

Growing out of the experience at the Military Hospital in Cobourg and in other military installations, the importance of occupational therapy as a part of the treatment program for the rehabilitation of both physical and psychological casualities became manifest. The National Committee, through the efforts of Norman Burnette, an executive of the Metropolitan Life Insurance Co., of Ottawa, promoted the development of occupational therapy in civilian mental hospitals throughout Canada. Since there were not enough trained occupational therapists available, many of the mental hospitals took advantage of the special skills and interests of nursing staff, attendants and even patients to promote this work.

7. Public and Professional Education

The importance of improving the training of doctors and medical students in psychiatry and mental hygiene was emphasized from the beginning by Dr. C.F. Martin, the National Committee president and McGill dean of medicine. At first this was attempted by organizing short courses of lectures and demonstrations in the mental hospitals and especially in the psychiatric out-patient clinics at the TGH and the Royal Victoria Hospital in Montreal. Cash prizes were awarded annually to medical students attaining the highest standing in psychiatry. Later much more intensive post-graduate training was made possible by securing travelling scholarships from such foundations as the Rockefeller. Selected physicians were enabled by this means to receive training in the United States, England and Europe. It took another twenty-five years to develop adequate post-graduate training in Canadian universities and mental hospitals.

Public education was recognized as a basic program area in order to try to develop a rational and intelligent attitude towards mental illness. Stigma and prejudice were prevalent and deeply rooted. Attempts to change public attitude through education were many and varied, including public lectures, newspaper articles and the wide distribution of pamphlets. *The Canadian Journal of Mental Hygiene,* edited by Dr. Gordon S. Mundie, of Montreal, Associate Medical Director of the National Committee, was published quarterly, beginning in May 1919. The journal was continued until 1921 when it was merged with *Mental Hygiene*, published by the American Committee. In its place a mental hygiene bulletin was published in 1920 to be used as a medium to inform the public as to the nature of the work of the Canadian National Committee.

A Mental Hygiene Exhibit was prepared in 1923 and was displayed in a major department store window in Montreal and used in many places during the years which followed.

8. Hincks Threatens Exposé

Most of the public education was carried out by Hincks in his public addresses. His crusading zeal was often evident in his impassioned oratory. Despite his policy of confidentiality with reference to reports to government, occasionally his exasperation with official *laissez-faire* led to emotional outbursts One of these landed him in trouble. In 1920 Hincks had an interview with The Honourable H.G. Nixon, the Ontario Provincial Secretary. He felt that Nixon was disinterested in the obvious problems facing the asylums and the mentally disordered. He left the interview discouraged and very angry. Later the same day, addressing a large audience of teachers at the annual convention of the Ontario Education Association, he blasted the government for its lack of concern and told the teachers he had enough scandalous information to "blow up the Parliament Buildings." The *Toronto Star* on April 1, 1920, gave this statement headline treatment and Hincks was in trouble!

Howard Ferguson was then the leader of the Opposition, and the next day on the floor of the House he waved a copy of the *Star* at Premier Drury and demanded to know who this character was. "Probably an immigrant," he suggested, and if so "he should be deported." Drury indicated that for once he could agree with the leader of the Opposition.

Hincks went to see Joseph E. Atkinson, publisher of the *Toronto Star,* and persuaded him to help obtain an interview with Premier Drury. Drury called Nixon and some others and Hincks told his story about the conditions in the mental hospital again. This time Nixon agreed that the conditions were indeed as Hincks described and Drury apologized. He agreed to table without comment a report on the situation, prepared by Hincks. This was published in the press and Hincks' reputation and that of the National Committee were saved. The Medical Officer of Health, Dr. C.J.O. Hastings, wrote to Hincks:

> My experience has taught me that it is not uncommon to have to explode a shell and then sit back and watch those concerned run for cover, but experience has taught us further that nothing but an impending calamity or a real explosion will arouse people to a sense of their duty, either individually or collectively.[22]

9. Summary

The first five years (1918-23) may be regarded as the period of early development. Surveys were conducted in every province concerning the care and treatment of people suffering from mental disorders. Fairly complete inspections of mental hospitals were made in all provinces, except for Ontario and Quebec, at the requests of provincial governments. The extent of mental disorder was found to be greater than expected, and preventive programs were non-existent.

In accordance with the Committee's recommendations, provincial governments spent over $6 million in improving facilities for the mentally ill. Surveys of school children in connection with mental deficiency were conducted in several centres in Ontario and Quebec. Over 150 special classes for retarded children were established by school boards.* Mental hygiene clinics were promoted and in some cases partially supported. A study of the psychiatric screening of immigrants resulted in a reduction of the number of new Canadians with mental disorders. The problem of "shell shock" and the rehabilitation of soldiers suffering from mental and nervous disorders was addressed through co-operation with DSCR and the Director General of Medical Services in the army. A beginning was made on public and professional education in mental hygiene and psychiatry.

---

*The idea of special classes for retarded children of course, is now obsolete; newer procedures designed to "normalize" such children in the community are now advocated.

III

The First
Scientific Programs
1924-33

1. The Development of Research

Toward the end of its first five years, the National Committee began to encounter difficulties. Funds were scarce. The death of the intrepid leader of Canadian psychiatry, Dr. C.K. Clarke, was a serious loss. The continuing surveys of mental hospitals, while important, took much time and could not be easily financed by a non-governmental agency. Dr. C.M. Hincks assumed the executive responsibility as Medical Director and immediately started planning a revitalized program and new funding.

He began by approaching large American foundations. The story of his success in obtaining grants is told elsewhere.[1] In addition, he continued to approach private supporters and organized limited public fund-raising campaigns in Canada which also proved successful. As a result, the Committee planned a new three-pronged program:

1. Funding of mental health and hygiene research in Canadian universities.

2. Raising standards of university training in mental health and psychiatry.

3. Arranging fellowships for the post-graduate training in Europe and the United States of potential leaders in psychiatry and mental hygiene.

An interesting example of how all these three program activities were simultaneously involved is provided by British Columbia. In 1925 this province appointed a Royal Commission to investigate the problem of mental retardation (mental deficiency). The National Committee offered to assist and the provincial government readily accepted the offer. The final report of the Commission acknowledged this assistance.

> The Provincial Government accepted the generous offer of the Canadian National Committee for Mental Hygiene to aid in prevention and treatment of mental abnormality in this Province, by:
>
> (a) Contributing the sum of $2,500 annually for a period of five years for research in mental hygiene at the University of British Columbia, or elsewhere in the province under the auspices of the University, provided the Provincial Government will contribute an equal sum.
>
> (b) Arranging for a special course of training at suitable centers on this continent, on the basis of a Rockefeller scholarship without cost to the province, for the man to be selected as Superintendent of the proposed Training School for Mental Deficients. The Commissioners desire to place on record their sincere appreciation of the aid extended to them in the course of their inquiry by many individuals and

organizations, among whom may be mentioned:

The Canadian National Committee for Mental Hygiene, with headquarters at Toronto, which placed at the Commission's disposal the resources of their organization and arranged for a personal survey of its problems by their Medical Director, Dr. C.M. Hincks, resulting in much valuable counsel and advice, and also for the visit of Mr. D.M. LeBourdais, Director of the Division of Education, who has been of great assistance to this Commission and has addressed many meetings throughout the Province on the subject of mental hygiene.[2]

Surveys of provincial services for the care and treatment of the mentally ill and the training and education of the retarded continued as time and staff permitted. The new research and training programs were developed chiefly at the University of Toronto in the Department of Psychology and at McGill University in the Department of Psychology and the Medical Faculty, and later (1929) in McGill's Mental Hygiene Institute, and in the University of Alberta and the University of Saskatchewan. In all these centres considerable emphasis was placed on the longitudinal life study of young, apparently normal children. Closely related to this was parent education for childrearing from a mental health point of view. Other studies concerned the education of nurses, social workers, and medical students in the field of normal personality development, consultation with social agencies in the management of problem cases, and studies of apparently healthy public-school populations of children and their families.

2. Projects at the University of Toronto

At the University of Toronto, the plan of research was devised by a committee comprising the members of the Department of Psychology and representatives of other university departments, the National Committee, and various participating community agencies. The committee was chaired by Professor J.G Fitzgerald, Director of the School of Hygiene. Cooperating with the Department of Psychology were the Board of Education, the Toronto Department of Public Health, the Infants Home, the Juvenile Court, and the Hospital Training School at Orillia, among others. Several projects involving research, education and service with the community were begun. In this development, E.A Bott, the professor and head of the Department of Psychology, became the leader. As early as 1924, he was disscussing the possible role of psychology in mental health.

In 1924 the Canadian National Committee for Mental Hygiene received a grant from the Rockefeller Foundation for a five year period of study upon problems concerning the mental health of school-age children. This assistance, supplemented by Canadian funds contributed for the same purpose, enabled the Committee to organize two research divisions in co-operation with Canadian Universities. In this departure the Committee's aim of strengthening our University personnel for research and teaching in the field of mental hygiene and at the same time of accumulating knowledge useful for institutions and agencies which have to cope with the practical phases of these problems the country over, is proving a sound and practical policy.

Investigation must extend beyond the individual in the narrower sense, into the whole network of circumstances which affect him. How to apply scientific methods to the study of those manifold settings in daily life where difficulties of human adjustment take their rise, is one of the open challenges of our time to modern science. The answer has yet to be found and should be sought through experimentation.

From its inception the research division at Toronto has

stressed exploration in order to determine what problems and methods are most suitable for investigation by co-operation between a university and community organizations. Within the university assistance and guidance is similarly secured from all of those departments whose technical interests are represented in any of the studies.[3]

It is interesting that the newly-strengthened Department of Psychiatry and the newly-opened Toronto Psychiatric Hospital were not represented on this research committee although Dr. Fitzgerald as Dean of the School of Hygiene was closely affiliated with the Medical faculty. Undoubtedly the passing of Dr. Clarke at this critical stage must have had an influence.

(a) The Nursery School and the Institute for Child Study

Prof. E.A. Bott, recalling how the St. George's nursery school established its emphasis on mental hygiene and primary prevention, wrote as follows:

> The major advance of child study in Canada came only after the war of 1914-18, and was in large part an outgrowth of the re-education methods and psychological principles that were developed for the muscle-function training of crippled veterans at the University of Toronto during 1916-19, namely, that a patient must not remain passive and psychologically dependent, but must become a participant learner, if he is to master his present limitations and thus be able to meet later situations with confidence. In the case of children, the age was earlier and the tasks simpler than with veteran patients, but the motivation with emphasis on self-direction and progressive achievement was similar in the two undertakings.
>
> The potential leadership to pioneer in this new field was not wanting locally. Having contributed greatly in the re-education programme for veterans, Mr. Blatz saw also its

broader implications. He readily grasped the idea, first, that these same principles should apply in dealing with persons through all stages of life, and second, that the early stages of this learning process should be the most basic period for study and application. To prepare himself for this broader field of endeavour he planned immediately to complete his medical degree at Toronto (having an honours M.A.), and then to take his Ph.D. in basic psychology under Carr at the University of Chicago, which he did in 1924.[4]

At about the same time, through the Canadian National Committee for Mental Hygiene, the support of the Rockefeller Foundation was secured for a five-year grant for the study of mental hygiene problems in public school children in Toronto, and of the Laura Spelman Rockefeller Memorial for a project concerning the study of pre-school children. Dr. Blatz returned from Chicago to take part in these projects and assumed the Directorship of St. George's School for Child Study, which was opened during the academic year 1925-26 in a renovated private home at 47 St. George Street. From the beginning this experiment was organized in two sections, a Nursery School Division and a Parent Education Division, each with a separate staff under the Director. It opened at first on a Laura Spelman Memorial grant under the general sponsorship of the University Department of Psychology, with a management committee on which several university departments were represented. Five years later, under a further grant, the School was moved to larger quarters. . . 96-98 St. George Street. In 1938 St. George's School was taken into the university and became administratively distinct from the Department of Psychology. It thus became the Institute of Child Study, an independent unit under the University of Toronto, in charge of a Committee of the Senate on which

Clifford Whittingham Beers (1876-1943), founder in 1908 of the
Mental Hygiene Movement in America.

Source: CMHA Collection, QSMHC Archives

Dr. Charles Kirk Clarke (1857-1924), Medical Director and co-founder with Dr. C.M. Hincks in 1918 of the Canadian National Committee for Mental Hygiene (1918).

Source: CMHA Collection, QSMHC Archives

Dr. Clarence Meredith Hincks (1885-1964), Secretary and then
General Director of the Canadian National Committee for Mental
Hygiene.

(Photo: 1950)
Source: CMHA Collection, QSMHCM Archives

Dr. Charles Ferdinand Martin (1868-1953), the first President of the Canadian National Committee for Mental Hygiene (1918-1937).

were represented the faculties or departments that are mainly concerned.

The Nursery School provided successive groups of children of pre-school age (from two to five years) for intensive observation and study in close collaboration with their parents. The longitudinal study plan began with the collection of data concerning the individual child from birth and continued as far as possible throughout life. The data recorded was of course arbitrarily selected according to principles of developmental and behavioural psychology popular at that time. Blatz and his colleagues, particularly Helen Bott (the wife of Professor E.A. Bott), added their own concepts and principles relating to child psychology, growth, and development, in connection with the appetites, attitudes, and learning. The basic functions of the school were research and teaching. It was confidently believed that the experience in the nursery school was beneficial and of mental hygiene value to the child. The division of parent education provided parents with knowledge and experience in raising and managing their children in wise and healthy ways. Dr. Dorothy Millichamp described the nursery school functions as follows:

> When St. George's School started, goals were specified, but there was little knowledge of the best means of accomplishing these. The Director, writing in 1926, stated the case: "A special technique for dealing with this age has to be evolved. In the meantime the children are enjoying an atmosphere of freedom, self-dependence, regulated habits, adequate social contacts and of serenity. The latter is the sine qua non of any well-conducted Nursery School." These goals have not altered but it has taken the Institute twenty-five years of study and practical experience to re-define "freedom," "self-dependence," "regulated habits," "social contacts," and finally "serenity" in terms of

childhood meaning. The history of the Nursery School is largely the story of increasing knowledge and deepening understanding of the child, giving rise to growing wisdom in his management.[5]

(b) The Regal Road School Project

The second major project at Toronto was also directed by Dr. Blatz. With the co-operation of the Toronto Board of Education, a public school comprising some 1,400 children was designated for the intensive study of mental health principles. The Canadian Medical Association's report[6] described this project as follows:

> The educational research which is part of the research at Regal Road School includes the recording of the major educational facts concerning each child. Techniques for overcoming educational difficulties are discussed with the teacher concerned. New measures for psychometric work are being sought. Data are being collected to clarify the psychological analysis in its relation to efficiency in school. Studies were made to evaluate success in terms other than content-examinations. A modification of the Dalton Plan★ was instituted in one classroom.
>
> The Regal Road research has brought about certain results related to the rest of the research work, which may be expressed as follows:
>
> (1) Training of a staff capable of carrying on such research. When work was started, funds seemed to be the primary need, but when funds were made available, it was soon found that workers were not, so it was necessary to

---

★The Dalton Plan was a scheme that encouraged the child to set his own goals of accomplishment desired within a given time. This was a kind of contract which the child accepted in return for being free of any pressure or even teaching process except whenever he or she wished help or direction.

train staff, and this training has become an integral part of the programme.

(2) Development of a method or technique for observation and the recording of longitudinal studies. This includes a record of all items which bring the child into conflict with authority in the school or elsewhere, a record of the home environment, the intelligence and the personality of the child.

(3) Making available potentially valuable data. The records of over three hundred and fifty children are sufficiently complete to justify their being followed for a period of years, in order to reconcile adult life adjustments with observations made during school life, and to determine if the genesis of maladjusted adult life lies in childhood.

(4) Development of methods of treating some of the common problems which arise in school. This service has not been extensively developed because, in general, it was desired to observe rather than to attempt to correct.

(5) Extensive use of the findings of the research in the university teaching.

(6) Preparation of a book, covering the findings of the research. Previously used for professional training these findings will now be made available to the reading public on publication of the book.[6]*

Dr. Blatz was convinced of the value of the lifetime longitudinal records kept on so many children. In the case of the nursery school these records were usually started by the mothers of children at the time of their birth or even before. Blatz referred to the banks of records as a "gold mine for future research" into the nature and development of mental illness and thus to the possibilities of prevention.

Other research in Toronto, sponsored and partially

---

*No book has yet been published but research reports and a monograph have appeared.[7] [8]

funded by the National Committee, included studies on Industrial Psychology,[9] on the Social Psychology of boys' gangs and street groups,[10] and Educational Psychology[11] involving teacher training and consultation on curriculum planning.

3. Projects in Montreal

In Montreal a small group of interested people had organized a branch of the National Committee in 1919. CNCMH was reluctant to expand in this way but decided to support this one branch. Dr. Gordon Mundie, Professor of Neurology at McGill became the branch director and subsequently the Associate Medical Director of the National Committee and editor of the Canadian Journal of Mental Hygiene.

Dr. Baruch Silverman joined the branch as a volunteer in 1923 and persuaded Dr. Mundie to let him open a Mental Hygiene Clinic patterned after the Child Guidance Clinics in the United States.* This clinic, like Dr. Clarke's clinic in Toronto, became enormously busy and useful to the Montreal schools and social agencies.

From the beginning of these activities research possibilities were kept in mind. With more funds now available from the National Committee a nursery school and a parent education project was initiated in Montreal similar to the Toronto program. Dr. Mundie died in 1926 and was succeeded by Dr. W.T.B. Mitchell. Unfortunately the nursery school had to close after five years due to

---

*Child Guidance clinics, sponsored by the Commonwealth Fund in the USA were usually staffed by a multi-discipline team, comprising a psychiatrist, a psychologist and a social worker. Mental health clinics in Canada quickly adopted this same pattern.

shortage of funds.

Surveys for the Montreal Protestant School Board had been completed and published with results similar to the Toronto studies and Harriet Mitchell, wife of Dr. Mitchell carried on a lively program of parent and family life education.

With the closing of the nursery school, the Montreal group together with the National Committee decided to organize a Mental Hygiene Institute[12] for purposes of research, education and clinical services to the community. It was directed by Dr. Mitchell, and is described on page 51.

As in Toronto, research involved longitudinal studies. There were over five hundred new cases a year. Special interest was directed to the role of the environment as a cause of abnormal behavior. Considerable attention was given to the instruction of undergraduate university students, nurses, and teachers as well as the professional staffs of the social agencies.

The National Committee provided funds to help pay the staff not only of the Mental Hygiene Committee but also that of psychologists working in the McGill Faculty of Medicine. Professor and Mrs. J.W. Bridges joined the university in 1924 to assist in mental hygiene teaching and research. The teaching of medical students was in the fields of normal and abnormal psychology and personality development. Research was directed to juvenile delinquency.

Similarly, by 1926 the services of Dr. David Slight were made available as professor of psychiatry. He was one of the first to introduce the teaching of psychiatry on the wards as well as in the psychiatric out-patient clinic at the Royal Victoria General Hospital.

4. Dr. Hincks Evaluates the Scientific Program

By the end of 1925 Dr. Hincks, now the Medical Director of the organization, was able to say in his annual report that there was underway a well-developed program of research:

A year and a half ago the National Committee embarked upon a research enterprise that would make possible the launching of a programme of prevention. It was decided to commence work in collaboration with McGill University, Montreal, and the University of Toronto. $80,000 per annum are being spent in these two centres and a research staff has been organized composed of eminent Canadian scientists. Intensive studies are being conducted that will lead us to a better understanding of conditions that are essential for the healthy mental and physical development of children. Our workers are enthusiastic in their endeavours and it would seem that important contributions will be made to scientific knowledge in the realm of mental hygiene. The Medical Director is one of the opinion that upwards of 25% of mental and nervous disorders are either caused or accentuated by unsatisfactory home and school methods that are now in vogue in child rearing. It is possible that Canada, as a result of research studies, will assume a degree of world leadership in fighting mental abnormality.

The sub-committee in charge of the research programme in Montreal consists of officers of the National Committee and of McGill University and, in Toronto, the sub-committee is composed similarly of representatives of our National organization and of the University.

The research work to be successful depends upon many factors. It is all important, among other things, to have the services of men and women who are well trained for the specific studies they undertake. Through the kindness of the Rockefeller Foundation and of the Laura Spelman Rockefeller Memorial, a dozen Canadians will have the advantage of training under fellowships in the

United States and Europe.

A new enterprise of significance is the inauguration, in an experimental way, of parent instruction in child rearing. The Metropolitan Life Insurance Company has made an initial grant for the purpose and the work will commence immediately in affiliation with research activities in Toronto and Montreal.[13]

The Medical Director's annual report for 1926 gave more details.

> We have conducted a survey for the Nova Scotia Government; co-operated with the Mental Hygiene Commission of the British Columbia Government; co-operated with the Manitoba Government in providing a travelling clinic for that Province and have been active in various ways throughout Canada.
>
> The Nova Scotia survey brought to light the fact that mental deficiency is on the increase. In one school community no less than 8% were feebleminded. Some of the institutions of the province were a disgrace. In collaboration with Premier Rhodes and the Attorney General, The Honourable Mr. Hall, definite steps will be taken in 1927 to meet the serious state of affairs connected with mental deficiency.
>
> Aside from our National service we are making excellent progress in building up research organizations in McGill University and the University of Toronto. We have sixteen psychologists and psychiatrists at work and a programme is being outlined for the prevention of mental and nervous disorders. This is not only a significant development in mental hygiene in Canada, but significant in the realm of inter-university relationship and the promotion of science generally.
>
> We have meted out thirteen fellowships to Canadians, on Rockefeller money, who have returned or will be returning to Canada to give leadership in mental hygiene in various parts of the country.[14]

Three years later (1929) Dr. Hincks' exuberance and optimism were running high. Referring particularly to the work at the universities in Toronto and McGill his annual report stated:

> Studies at these two centres are revealing practical means for the prevention of mental disorders. The investigations are paving the way for the adoption throughout Canada of measures that will reduce the tremendous burden of mental disability - a burden that is as great as physical disease. You will realize the significance of undertakings at McGill and Toronto by a consideration of two facts. Between 4 and 5 per cent of all Canadian school children will become insane sooner or later in the absence of preventive measures and will be admitted to our mental hospitals. . .*
>
> The research at McGill and Toronto is important therefore and has attracted the interest of scientists from all over the world. This research is as necessary for the welfare of Canada as medical research in physical disabilities.[15]

5. Universities of Alberta and Saskatchewan

In 1929 the National Committee was also able to give modest grants in aid of "mental hygiene research" to the Universities of Alberta and Saskatchewan. In Alberta the key person directing research in this field was Prof. J.M. MacEachran of the Department of Philosophy. His influence on students of education and teachers was tremendous. Although neither a psychologist nor a psychiatrist, he was able to engender great enthusiasm and interest in student teachers about mental hygiene. In Saskatchewan Prof. S.R. Laycock of the Faculty of

---

*Such extravagant predictions seemed accurate enough at the time. The development of new policies and services since 1960 have fortunately improved the mental health prospects for children somewhat.

Education was directing research in personality and behaviour maladjustments of school children and in the attitudes of teachers toward such problems. In both Edmonton and Saskatoon the research sponsored by the National Committee contributed directly to the development of mental health services in the school system.

Reporting on the annual meeting the CNCMH bulletin (January and November 1930) referred to these activities thus:

E.A. Bott. Professor of Psychology, University of Toronto, stated: "Broadly the outlook is psychological, but actually the organization is a co-operative one, aiming to unite the efforts of scientists interested in mental hygiene and to establish contacts in the community for their work. Psychology and mental hygiene," he said, "are not identical, but they are significantly complementary. To understand ordinary people, whatever their stage and station in life, and to assist them in ways that make for better mental health, largely by educational means, is now a recognized major objective in mental hygiene."

The opening, in October, 1929, of the Mental Hygiene Institute of Montreal at 531 Pine Avenue West, marks an important step forward in the promotion of mental health in Montreal; and it should exert a helpful influence upon mental hygiene progress throughout the Dominion generally. It is located in an attractive two-storey building provided by McGill University; and is a direct outgrowth of the work formerly carried on by the Mental Hygiene Committee of Montreal. Its establishment is due to the co-operation and financial support, jointly, of the University, the Montreal Council of Social Agencies, and the CNCMH.

Since its aim is the prevention of nervous and mental disease, delinquency, and crime, it is essential that these forms of behaviour should be recognized and dealt with while yet in their initial stage. It is therefore important that an ever-increasing number of physicians, parents, social workers, and teachers should become familiar with known principles of mental health and their application. In this regard the Institute is unique: it is the only training-centre of its kind in Canada. As a local agency it is, through the Montreal Council of Social Agencies, concerned with the mental health of people in and about Montreal; but through the interest of the CNCMH, it is concerned with the training of physicians, nurses, and social workers for service in other parts of Canada. In its integration with the University, it is part of the Department of Preventive Medicine; the Director and Assistant Director are members of the staff of the Department. In this way the benefits of the Institute are made available to the students.

"In the University of Alberta in addition to the regular courses in the Faculty of Arts and Sciences, special courses in Psychology embodying the general outlook and main principles of mental hygiene are provided for all professional faculties," said Dr. MacEachran, Professor of Philosophy. "For students in Medicine, Dentistry, Nursing, and Education, such courses are compulsory. In the school of Education, which is organized within the Faculty of Arts and Sciences, the professional training involves a solid grounding in philosophy beginning in the second year and running throughout the whole course. . . All teachers in training are required to attend a certain number of clinics in mental hygiene. . .

One of the main objectives of the mental hygiene work centred in the University is the training of personnel, and this will perhaps be the most important aspect of the work during the next few years. Funds provided by the CNCMH are used mainly for this purpose. An effort is being made to select students whose interests and ability point to careers in Psychiatry, Psychology, Social Work and Education. The most promising of these receive fellowships and are employed during the summer in connection with government clinics and the public institutions."

Dr. Sam R. Laycock, Professor of Educational Psychology, University of Saskatoon, reported on two research projects he is conducting in that province. (1) Research in the Personality and Behaviour Maladjustments of School Children; and (2) Teachers' Reactions to Personality and Behaviour Maladjustments of School Children.

Dr. Laycock believes that the study of childhood should be "diagnostic in attitude and longitudinal as well as cross-sectional in method," and his first step was to build up a case file for each of the 550 school children studied.

IV

Strengthening the Structure 1926

1. The Legal Charter

On December 1, 1926 the National Committee became formally and legally incorporated under Letters Patent. The Letters Patent set out the purpose of the Canadian National Committee for Mental Hygiene and provided its Dominion Charter. These have remained essentially unchanged to this day, although changes in the name of the organization and in several of the by-laws have been made.

The objects of the Corporation are to ensure the best possible care, treatment and rehabilitation of the mentally ill and the mentally disabled; to strive to prevent mental illness and mental disability; to promote research into their causes, treatment and prevention; to protect and promote mental health and in execution of the foregoing to secure the support of the public and to co-operate with other agencies and associations both professional and lay, working in these and related fields, and to urge governments at all levels to take legislative and financial action to further these objectives.

Although there were in existence at that time a provincial Society for Mental Hygiene in Nova Scotia and a Mental Hygiene Council in New Brunswick, in addition to the Montreal branch, it was decided for the time being not to proceed further with the organization of provincial or local branches. Such development did not come about for another twenty-five years.*

2. Hincks Goes to Europe

It was in 1926, the year of incorporation, that Clarence Hincks planned a trip to Britain and other European countries. Although he had worked for several years in clinical settings under the direction of Dr. C.K. Clarke and had acquired considerable experience in assessing mental hospital treatment programs and administration, he had never had the opportunity of seeing the famous psychiatric clinics in Europe or of meeting some of the world leaders in this field who were responsible for them. He had arranged for many Canadian doctors and other professionals to receive post-graduate training in these centres, but he had not had the opportunity himself. Through the generosity of the Rockefeller Foundation, he received a six-month travelling fellowship and proceeded at once to England. His mother had recently died and he decided to take with him his father, the distinguished Methodist clergyman, the Rev. William D. Hincks DD. On this trip his father would sometimes accompany him on his visits to meet famous people. They both went to Albert Hall to witness a

---

*See chapter XV, section 4, p. 205

demonstration by Emile Coué, the French chemist who had established a reputation for helping people suffering from mental health problems through a form of autosuggestion. His famous slogan was "Every day in every way I am getting better and better." At this demonstration several persons with very bad stuttering defects were able to speak perfectly fluently after Coué's ministrations.

Dr. Hincks visited other well known psychiatrists and psychologists, incuding Bernard Hart whose small book *The Psychology of Insanity*[1] had won him world-wide renown. He also met Dr. A.F. Tredgold whose book on mental deficiency was equally well-known.[2] Dr. Tredgold's views on sterilization as an eugenical approach to mental deficiency must have surprised and disturbed Hincks.[3] He had previously been deeply influenced in favour of sterilization by Dr. Helen MacMurchy. Tredgold's strong opposition to it led him to publish a summary of his (Tredgold's) views in the bulletin of the Canadian National Committee. Later, Hincks changed his mind again, when he discovered in 1928 that his colleagues in Alberta were ready to pass legislation allowing sterilization, especially in mentally retarded girls. The results of this practice over the next few years satisfied the Alberta authorities that the procedure was sound. The Act was rescinded in the mid-1970s, but Hincks never did change his mind again.

Among the places visited which left a lasting impression on Clarence Hincks were the famous York Retreat, a mental hospital established by the Quakers in the early 19th Century; the Belgian town of Gheel, a community devoted to the care of the mentally ill patients in private homes; the Bergholzli Clinic in Zürich and its director, Dr. Hans Maier; and, of course, the famous

Munich Psychiatric Institute directed by Dr. Emile Kraepelin. Dr. Kraepalin impressed Hincks deeply, as indeed he had Dr. C.K. Clarke during the latter's visit to Europe some years previously. Hincks recorded his impressions as follows:

My visit with Kraepelin was delightful. I was taken to the Research institute that he had established with money donated by Kaiser Wilhelm. It had taken Kraepelin fifteen years to assemble his group of research scientists. At the time of my visit, these scientists were in a sad plight financially because the money the Kaiser had given them had become almost worthless after the First World War. I told Professor Kraepelin that it would be a disaster if his research institute folded up and, with his permission, I would be glad to attempt to raise money for him in the United States. Kraepelin said, "Would you, who belong to a country that fought us in the last tragic war, come to the aid of a German research team?" I replied that science knows no boundaries or enemies. When I returned home, I secured a large grant for the Kraepelin Institute. I discussed many things with Dr. Kraepelin including his estimate of Sigmund Freud and if he thought we would ever be able to prevent and cure mental illnesses. In regard to Freud, he demonstrated no personal jealousy. He said that if Freud had been working with the psychoses as he (Kraepelin) had and not with the neuroses, Freud would never have been able to develop his interesting theories. As to whether we would ever be able to prevent and cure mental illness, Kraepelin said, "Through research, we will discover in time all the answers concerning the true nature and control of mental disabilities; but these answers will not come in your life time nor in mine. We will learn to prevent these disorders before we learn to cure them. If I had my life over and over again, I would enter your field of mental hygiene because it offers the greatest promise for prevention and I would be able to see concrete results before my death. My own daughter is in mental hygiene work and I am presently engaged in the allied field of industrial psychology." Thus spoke the great Kraepelin just a year before his death.[4]

His visit to England exposed him to Freudian psychoanalysis. In a remarkable letter to the president, Dr. Charles Martin, dated December 19, 1925, he wrote:

The last two weeks have been the most interesting in my scientific life. For years I have avoided coming to grips with psycho-analysis. Essentially I am a timid creature. I am lacking in courage. I dislike facing issues and will run around the block any time to avoid an unpleasant task. When, however, I actually enter a contest with myself, or anyone else, I am impelled by my unfortunate make-up to fight to a finish. I can well remember avoiding for years the question of religion and immortality. At last I faced these important and vital issues. For two years I devoted every ounce of energy in my being to reading, searching, thinking, and experimenting with myself to find a conclusion or at least peace of mind. Finally I arrived at much the same position as Sir William Osler. With him I could say, "On all these questions I have come to the conclusion that I cannot furnish myself with any scientific answer. I prefer, however, to believe in immortality even if I am wrong than not to believe even if non-belief is right." (Not Osler's exact words.) My two years' fight was worth while because I found peace of mind.

Thank Heaven, my wrestling with the problem of psycho-analysis lasted only two weeks and not two years. I made up my mind to accept Freudian conceptions and live absolutely under their influence for the time being. I swallowed without criticism the view that neuroses were due to mental conflict - that conflict arose because of conscious repression of archaic unconscious ideas - that these unconscious ideas had to do with incest passion for the parent of the opposite sex - that relief came through sublimation. I'll admit that it took some stern self-discipline to accept this formula but Jung made it easier by saying that the incest urge was not really sexual but a desire for spiritual rebirth.

Having accepted the standpoint, I plunged into psycho-analytic thought. I read Jung's *Psychological Types and Psychology of the Unconscious*, J.T. MacCurdy's *Psychology of the Emotions* and went to lectures by such well-known psycho-analysts as Ernest Jones, James Glover, and Creighton Miller.

Strange as it may seem I absolutely fell under the spell of this school of thought. My experience can be likened to religious conversion. Perhaps it would be nearer the truth to say that I got into a paranoid condition with delusions of grandeur. I felt that I had discovered a key to the human soul. With this key I could unlock the mysteries of the unconscious, the philosophies of the ages, and the impelling forces that have created the great religions. I believed that I had a mission in life. I would spend my time in interpreting the Bible to theologians and would start with the book of Revelations because Revelations is a glorious field for the psycho-analyst with its wealth of symbolism. I would organize classes in literature and take up the very works that in the past had been hardest to explain. If I had the time I would also heal the sick and show others the technique.

I found myself belittling the sympathetic nervous system, the endocrine glands, environment, and everything else that I had valued in the past as contributing factors to mental health or disease. I was sorry for my friends who had not received the divine light of revelation as I had received it.

Elton Mayo had told me before I left Canada how I could get out of such a trance if I ever fell victim. He said, "Read Pierre Janet." I did not want to come down to earth. Heaven was too sweet. I did not want to wake up. However, I took a big glass of an unprohibited drink in England and read Janet's *Principles of Psychotherapy*. I came to earth and reality with a bang!

I would not spend so much time on my individual

experience if it were not for the fact that mental hygiene and psychiatry are going through troublesome times in Europe and America. There is a fight between the psycho-analytic school of thought and those who do not belong to this school. The latter are in the minority - so far as thinking psychiatrists are concerned: the leader, Pierre Janet, a man who is so great that I want to brush up my French so that at least I can read his work if I cannot talk to him. Pierre Janet did the pioneer work that gave Freud his start. Janet realized the role of psychological analysis and repression in certain cases but his intelligence forbade him making the sweeping generalizations of Freud.

As I say, the Freudians are in the majority. Some of my dearest and most intellectual friends in the United States are standard-bearers. Some of the brightest minds in Europe are advocates.

What are we going to do in Canada? If we accept psycho-analysis as it is accepted by its advocates today, we will automatically rule out two thirds of worthwhile psychiatry, psychology, as applied to mental states. Psycho-analysis does not fuse with other forms of thought. In a paper by James Glover last night at the Royal Society of Medicine (Medical Section of the British Psychological Association), it was shown that psycho-analysis must stand by itself - just as Christian Science is a failure if you try to mix it with an affirmation of matter. Everybody clapped Glover on the back and said he was right.

I asked what are we going to do? I for one would like to throw in my lot with Pierre Janet, and Elton Mayo is his great exponent in America. Please read Janet's *Principles of Psychology* - George Allan and Unwin Limited, publishers. You will see the saneness of Janet's point of view and will realize how mental medicine can be linked up with the whole body of medicine. You will also see along what profitable lines we can conduct research in Canada - lines that have been neglected because of the dominance of psycho-analytic thought.

I would advise, however, that my psychiatric friends

take a real whirl at psycho-analysis - if they have not already done so. It will do them good because there is much value in this school. If they do not come out of the trance, they will at least be happy and they can earn five guineas an hour in London, $30.00 an hour in New York, $20.00 an hour in Vienna and perhaps $20.00 in Montreal and Toronto. That is some compensation. As a matter of fact, we need several psycho-analysts in Canada, but I hope they will not get control of our Mental Hygiene Movement.[5]

3. The Education Program

The public and professional education, which was initiated early in the history of the National Committee, continued throughout the 1920's. D.M. LeBourdais joined the staff as a "publicist" and the impact of his efforts was immediately apparent in the quality of the bulletin. For a while it was published almost monthly and carried many interesting articles. Some form of regular national newsletter under various names has continued ever since.

In addition, various pamphlets on aspects of child training and child management were prepared. Probably a high point in this activity was reached in 1928 when a series of seven lectures was delivered in Toronto and Montreal in collaboration with the University of Toronto and McGill University on the general theme of Mental Hygiene of Childhood. The first lecture was given by Dr. Charles F. Martin, the National President and Dean of Medicine at McGill. The others were given by distinguished psychiatrists from the United States. These were published as a booklet and received wide distribution.[6]

The annual meeting that year was held in Toronto and brought together a large group of mental hygiene professionals from across the country. Reports on mental hygiene research, especially in connection with children, were featured and widely reported. The next year Dr. W.E. Blatz presented a series of six lectures at Convocation Hall, University of Toronto, again on the subject of children. These proved so popular that arrangements were made for Dr. Blatz to repeat these lectures in several larger centres of Canada.

A similar series of lectures on children was presented by Dr. Baruch Silverman in Montreal in 1930.

4. Financing During the 1920s

The first attempts at fund-raising were the famous drawing-room meetings hosted by prominent women in Toronto and other major centres. During these gatherings, the invited groups were solicited for funds to finance a national program. This was surprisingly successful but, of course, self-limiting.

Hincks almost immediately began to visit wealthy industrialists and corporation executives, inviting them to become members of a Board of Directors and to pledge fairly large gifts over a three-year period. In this endeavour he freely referred to the encouragement he had received from the Governor General, the Duke of Devonshire, and from nationally-known physicians like Dr. C.F. Martin of McGill. This source of funds, while generous, was also seen to be time-limited. An approach was made to the Dominion (now Federal) Government for an annual grant. There was some reluctance to give support at first, but the truly impressive group of wealthy supporters who were now members of the Board finally convinced Ottawa to begin making annual grants. These have continued ever since. The first grant of $10,000 was made in 1919, and in 1928 this was increased to $20,000. By 1966 the annual federal grant had increased to $25,000 and in 1975 to $39,000. Since 1982 special funds have been made available in addition to the regular grants in order to finance important national preventive programs such as the mental health of workers in the workplace.*

Financing research and service projects with these funds had certain disadvantages. In the Department of Psychology at the University of Toronto, for example, nearly all the senior staff received a significant part of their salaries from the National Committee. Their obligations and responsibilities to the Committee were not always clear. On at least one occasion, overtures were made by a large university in the United States concerning the possibility of employing the entire group at greatly increased remuneration. The staff was tempted but did not want to leave Canada. In an effort to increase their personal incomes, the group urged Hincks to persuade one of his wealthy industrialist friends in Montreal to invest their savings in the stock market, which at that time (1926-28) was booming. Reluctantly Hincks and his friends did what they were asked, and the group doubled their money in a few months. They urged him to do it again, and again they increased their money by sizable amounts. Hincks and his Montreal friends refused to do it a third time. However, many of the group felt that by then, the early fall of 1929, they knew enough about the stock market to make it on their own. The stock market collapsed, they lost their investment, and they stayed in Canada![7]

---

*See chapter XIX, Section 4, and app. E

Various fund-raising plans were devised. In 1921 the "5000 Club" was sponsored by several Kiwanis clubs on behalf of the Committee. Each member of the "5000 Club" pledged $2.00 (or more) for the support of the mental hygiene movement, and it was decided that the number enrolled could easily be increased to 10,000. In addition, grants were received from the Canadian Red Cross Society and certain of the provinces for services rendered by the Committee.

Beginning in 1923, Dr. Hincks was able to establish close working conditions with the executives of the Rockefeller and other American foundations. Several of these executives became very good personal friends of Dr. Hincks. Included among these were Edwin Embree, a director and vice-president of the Rockefeller Foundation, and Beardsley Ruml, director of the Laura Spelman Rockefeller Memorial. Both these men spent considerable time in Canada with Hincks, exploring the possibility of providing support for research and service programs in mental health. By 1933 more than $335,000 had been received from these sources and invested in Canadian projects, mostly through the National Committee.

Hincks' policy was to match these foundation grants with money raised in Canada. In this connection he utilized schemes such as the "5000 Club" and government grants, but also special campaigns such as the Lady Byng of Vimy Fund launched by the wife of the Governor General on January 15, 1924. For this purpose a special meeting was convened in Montreal to which were invited leading politicians, industrialists, philanthropists, and scientists. The invitation to Prime Minister Mackenzie King included this paragraph:

On behalf of the Canadian National Committee for Mental Hygiene, I beg to extend an invitation to you to be present at a meeting in the Ball Room of the Ritz Carlton Hotel, Montreal, on Tuesday, January 15th, at 4:30 o'clock. The wife of our Governor General will formally launch for Canada The Lady Byng of Vimy Fund for Mental Hygiene. This fund will be utilized to introduce mental hygiene activities among children for the prevention of insanity and the control of feeble-mindedness; to promote scientific research in psychiatry; and, through educational measures, to secure better facilities for the treatment and control of mental abnormality throughout the Dominion.[8]

King never showed up; in fact he always seemed cautious about showing any personal interest in mental health and psychiatry.

V

International Activities
1930-31

1. The First International Congress

Ever since he organized the National Committee in the United States, Clifford Beers had been dreaming of a world wide congress of individuals and organizations interested and involved in the work of mental hygiene. When the Canadian Committee was started, he felt that the first step in this direction had been taken. There were, of course, professional organizations in several countries interested in mental disorders and their treatment. There were even a few voluntary societies, involving lay people. Most of these, however, had a specific orientation, such as mental retardation. What was needed was a clarion call for action on the treatment and prevention of mental disorders of all kinds, a call that could be heard throughout the world. Beers felt that Hincks and he together might be able to accomplish this. They started planning in the late 1920s. Finally, a new structure was established, The International Committee for Mental Hygiene.

Beers personally devoted a large part of his time to the promotion of this congress by corresponding with psychiatrists and mental health leaders throughout the world. A strong organizational committee was established and an unusual type of scientific program was planned - a format which has been followed pretty much in all world mental health congresses since. An article in the CNCMH bulletin, January, 1930, described the plans:

> An interesting as well as sensible innovation is the decision of the organization committee to dispense with the reading of papers, ordinarily such a tiresome feature of such conferences. All papers will therefore be printed - in English, French, German, and possibly Spanish also - and distributed to the members in advance. Each author will be asked to lead the discussion on his own paper, ten minutes being allowed him to present a summary of it. Supplementing these discussions, there will be informal sessions for the more thorough consideration of particular topics by those especially interested in them.
>
> The annual meetings of the American Psychiatric Association and the American Association for the Study of the Feebleminded will be held concurrently with the Congress. Fifty other allied associations will be represented.

In spite of the excellent people involved in the organizing committee, none had had experience in organizing a world congress. The arrangements became chaotic. Beers applied to the Department of U.S. Secretary of State for help, and they suggested that Beers contact Colonel H. Edmond Bullis. Bullis had achieved a reputation for organization in a number of fields and in many foreign countries. Beers persuaded him to take over the non-professional aspects of the congress, and this led to Bullis' interesting career in the mental health movement. He described the initial conversation he had with Beers early in 1930[1].

Mr. Beers proved to be a very intense, enthusiastic man in his early fifties. He said to me, "In May, here in Washington, the first International Congress on Mental Hygiene will be held. Scientific delegations representing important nations of the world will attend. I am looking for someone, experienced in dealing with groups from overseas, to make arrangements for the reception, entertainment and tours for these distinguished scientists. A secretary to a state department official has given me your name as having had experience with foreign missions. I would like to discuss this matter with you."

Mr. Beers told me something about the American National Committee for Mental Hygiene, which he had organized some twenty-one years before. He also told me that the Rockefeller Foundation, the Carnegie Corporation, and a number of wealthy philanthropists had advanced the money to finance the congress.

I agreed to work from my office in Washington for the next ten weeks, and assured Mr. Beers I would carry out the program as outlined. I sugggested an honorarium of $1,000 for my part time services, which was accepted by Mr. Beers. He then took me to St. Elizabeth's Hospital, the large federal mental hospital on the outskirts of Washington, where he introduced me to its superintendent, Dr. William A. White, who was president of the First International Congress on Mental Hygiene. I was very impressed with Dr. White, who was often referred to as the dean of American psychiatry.

Mr. Beers left with me the names of foreign delegates. The next day I drew up a list of important social leaders in Washington and narrowed this list to seven names, all of whom were regarded as important leaders in our national capital. I took this list over to Dr. White for his approval. He thought I had made an excellent selection, as he knew all of the seven.

His secretary was able to telephone five of those on my list. Dr. White asked them to serve on the Washington entertainment committee. They accepted. Within the next several days all seven had agreed to help make arrangements for the Washington entertainment of our congress delegates from other parts of the world.

I had a letterhead printed, showing the names of the officers of the congress - all distinguished psychiatrists from all parts of the world - and also listing the names of the Washington entertainment committee. On this letterhead I wrote to all the legations and embassies in Washington of those countries sending delegates to the congress, asking that receptions, teas, luncheons or dinners be arranged for their nationals while they were in Washington, and also for a few selected American guests. All the embassies and legations said they would cooperate.

Dr. White and I called upon President Hoover, who agreed to receive the congress delegates in the White House Rose Garden and to have his picture taken with them. Dr. Ray Lyman Wilbur, Secretary of the Interior, said he would give a reception at the Department of Interior, and Dr. White arranged for a tea at St. Elizabeth's and a tour of his hospital for those interested.

Mr. Beers had estimated that there would be about 1,600 delegates from 15 different countries at the congress. By April 1st the three hotels that had been reserved for congress delegates were filled up. I was asked to set up a housing bureau. Eventually more than 4,100 delegates from 51 different countries registered. By April 15 I was put in charge of all congress arrangements except the scientific program. I realized the ball rooms of the Willard and Washington Hotels would be inadequate, so I rented the Daughters of the American Revolution Constitution and Continental Halls.

★ ★ ★

The congress was a great success. On Wednesday evening at Constitution Hall, with President Hoover and delegates from all over the world present, 4,100 people rose to their feet and gave Clifford Beers a most enthusiastic ovation. It was the high point of his colourful life.

Colonel Bullis's success in managing the congress in 1930, led to his appointment as Executive Officer of the American National Committee, a position he held for many years.

An account of the congress written by D.M. Lebourdais was carried in the CNCMH bulletin in May, 1930. It stated in part:

> Mental Hygiene history was made when, during the week, May 5-10, representatives from fifty-three countries gathered at Washington D.C., for the First International Congress on Mental Hygiene and organized the International Committee for Mental Hygiene. That it is at all possible to draw twenty-five hundred persons from the world over to discuss common problems in human relations is a tribute to the vision, foresight and indefatigable enthusiasm of one man: Clifford W. Beers, who twenty-two years ago organized the first mental hygiene society in the world, and whose splendid dream of a world-wide association has really been achieved.

★ ★ ★

> Canadians played a large part in the Congress; Dr. C.M. Hincks, Medical Director, The Canadian National Committee for Mental Hygiene, was a member of the Committee on Organization, which during the past year, had grappled strenuously with the multitudinous details necessary to bring such a huge undertaking to a successful conclusion. Papers were read by Dr. Hincks; Dr. W.E. Blatz, Professor of Psychology, University of Toronto, (in absentia); Dr. A.T. Mathers, Provincial Psychiatrist, Province of Manitoba; Dr. W.T.B. Mitchell, Director, the Mental Hygiene Institute, Montreal; Dr. C.B. Farrar, Director, the Toronto Psychiatric Hospital; and by Dr. E.P. Lewis, Department of Public Health, Toronto. Dr. Hincks was elected one of the vice-presidents of the International

Committee for Mental Hygiene, and was delegated to speak at the International Luncheon on behalf of North America, when representatives of the six continents were called upon in turn. The Canadian delegation was, in number, second only to that of the United States.

2. Hincks Goes to New York

Following the International Congress, the U.S. National Committee for Mental Hygiene was reorganized. With Colonel Bullis as Executive Officer, it was decided that a new Medical Director was needed. Dr. Hincks was invited to fill this post. His own account of this event reveals the reservations he had about accepting the position and the compromises he proposed. These were approved and Dr. Hincks began his work for the U.S. National Committee almost immediately. He remained in this position until late 1938 when, with the international scene becoming cloudy and the personal tensions in the New York office becoming uncomfortable[2], Hincks decided to resume his full time duties in Canada. In his autobiography he wrote:

> In the spring of 1930, I received a long distance telephone call from New York asking me to attend the next day a meeting of the Board of Directors of the National (U.S.) Committee for Mental Hygiene. No reasons were given for this invitation. As soon as I arrived at the meeting, the President, Dr. Arthur Ruggles, asked me what I would do if I were General Director of the U.S. Committee. I told the Board at great length what I would do and I was then asked what range of responsibilities I would like to assume. My answer was to be responsible, under the Board, for program planning and execution, and for fund-raising. Members of the Board said that meant everything; and I replied, "Program planning without money is academic, and fund-raising without a sound program is deceiving the public." The Board was sceptical of my ability to assume both

functions, program and funding, because predecessors, Dr. Thomas Salmon and Dr. Frankwood Williams, had been responsible for programs only. Clifford Beers, as Secretary, had been the genius in raising necessary funds. The Board informed me that they already had a plan for raising money through a contract with one of the money-raising organizations - a contract that called for the raising by the company of one million dollars and the payment by the National Committee of $100,000 for the services, of which $25,000 had already been paid. I was asked what I would do under these circumstances, and I said that I would call upon the fund-raising organization and request them to cancel the contract because "this fund collecting company can raise millions of dollars for universities and hospitals but it cannot raise money for our work. The only method that will be successful for us is the method employed by Clifford Beers in this country and by me in Canada - the individual buttonholing of prospective donors." I was then asked to leave the board room. When I returned, Dr. Ruggles said, "The board has decided to offer you the post of Medical Director." I accepted on two conditions - first that, at the end of two years, the Board could terminate my services or I could resign, and second, that I could retain my Canadian post on half-time basis. These conditions were accepted; and I remained in United States's work for eight and a half years.[3]

It is not the purpose of this history to record or comment in detail on the work accomplished by Dr. Hincks while he was Medical Director of the U.S. National Committee. However, several of the projects in which he played a leading role related to both Canada and the United States.

(a) *Survey of Psychiatric Training*

It was decided to undertake a major study of the programs and facilities for psychiatric education and research in all Class A medical schools in the United States and Canada.

The suggestion for this five-year project (1932-37) came from Barry Smith, the Director of the Commonwealth Fund. With Commonwealth support, Hincks organized and implemented the survey. The work was done by several prominent psychiatrists, Franklin Ebaugh of the University of Colorado, Ralph Noble of Australia, and Charles A. Rymer.[4]

The survey made a significant contribution to the raising of the level of psychiatric teaching and research in North America. In Hincks' opinion:

> Along with the impetus of Freud's theories, it ushered in modern psychiatry as we know it today. And one of its chief results was the making of psychiatry into a respectable and helpful partner with medicine and surgery and the other subdivisions of medicine. This was brought about during the survey with frequent joint sessions between psychiatrists and representatives of other branches of medicine.[5]

(b) The Certification of Psychiatrists

Along with the raising of the status of psychiatry as a specialty was the certification of those doctors who had completed specified training and passed special examinations that indicated their proficiency as specialists, as was the case with medicine and surgery. In Dr. Hincks' words:

> For the protection of the public, we in the American National Committee advocated a national system for certification and one of the members of our staff Dr. Samuel Hamilton approached the American Medical Association on the subject. Dr. Hamilton got a favourable response and there was created the American Board of Psychiatry and Neurology, with succesful candidates receiving certification in psychiatry and/or neurology

according to qualifications. The American Board demanded four years' post-graduate work in psychiatry at approved training centers, followed by examinations. This plan has worked well over the years and has resulted in the development of psychiatry as a specialty with a status that is comparable to internal medicine and surgery. In Canada, the certifying Board is the Royal College of Physicians and Surgeons of Canada, which established the certification of specialists in psychiatry in 1945.[6]

(c) Funding Research into Schizophrenia

Melvin Johnson, a distinguished Boston lawyer and Sovereign Grand Commander of the Scottish Rite Masons in the northern United States, became interested in improving the usefulness of their benevolent funds. Through Edwin Embree who now was president of the Julius Rosenwald Fund, he made contact with Dr. Hincks and Colonel Bullis of the U.S. National Committee. After much negotiation, a plan was evolved in 1934 by which many thousands of dollars were spent each year in research grants for projects related to the understanding, the cause, the treatment, and the prevention (if possible) of what was then called dementia praecox (now schizophrenia). The National Committee contributed the scientific expertise for the selection of projects, the fieldwork and on-site visits which were necessary for their assessment. Among the Canadian projects financed by the Scottish Rite funds were the preparation of a Mental Hygiene textbook for teachers, a study of shy school children[7] [8] in Toronto, and a series of hormonal and biochemical studies relating to stress conducted at the Allan Memorial Institute, Montreal.[9]

It appeared to those working on the Canadian Committee that Hincks was spending much more than half the time in the States. Actually, he frequently returned to

Canada and at times it seemed he was commuting between Toronto and New York. Come summer he always returned for a long holiday to his beloved Muskoka home. The hurly-burly of New York was stimulating but as he often repeated, "My heart stays in Canada." With Hincks away so much, it became obvious that the Canadian staff needed strengthening and more precise direction. With the Great Depression settling in, the need for refinancing the program was apparent. Private philanthropy was dwindling, and renewed efforts were needed to obtain support from governments and large foundations. Dr. Grant Fleming, Professor of Public Health and Preventive Medicine at McGill University, was made Medical Director; Dr. C.B. Farrar, Professor of Psychiatry at the University of Toronto, and Dr. J.G. McKay, superintendent of a private mental hospital, Hollywood Sanitarium, in New Westminster, B.C., were made Associate Medical Directors. Miss Marjorie Keyes became the Executive Secretary. Dr. Hincks was made "Director," and finally "General Director," a title which persists today for the chief executive officer of the National Organization.

Special program divisions of the National Committee were organized, each with its own paid, part-time director. These were:

1. Education (including publicity), D.M. LeBourdais - a freelance journalist

2. Statistics and Legislation, Dr. H.B. Spaulding - a lawyer

3. Immigration, Dr. Helen R.Y. Reid - a public health physician

4. Quebec, Dr. A.H. Desloges - a health administrator.

Voluntary members of the committee chosen from the

medical, educational, and mental health professions provided supportive and technical advice to these divisional directors.

VI

Evaluation and
New Opportunities
1931-39

1. The Canadian Medical Association Survey

In spite of arrangements made to continue the vigorous program by the Canadian Committee, Hincks' absence in the United states caused increasing concern. There was no full-time professional person left to supervise the activities across the country, save the redoubtable Miss Marjorie Keyes, the resourceful nurse turned social worker, turned secretary, turned executive officer! Dr. Grant Fleming of McGill was particularly worried, so he and Dr. Hincks requested the Canadian Medical Association (CMA) to conduct a critical survey of the organization and its program. The CMA agreed and nominated Dr. J.G. Fitzgerald, Dean of Medicine at Toronto and Dr. Fleming to carry it out. Their report, parts of which have already been quoted, was published in 1932. The conclusions and recommendations included the following:

Conclusions:

It may be fairly stated that the Canadian National Commitee has materially contributed to securing the following:

A. The training of mental hygiene leaders.

B. Raising the standard of instruction for professional groups in universities.

C. Studies in the field of Parent Education.

D. Public education in mental hygiene.

E. Establishment of mental hygiene research in co-operation with universities, leading to a better understanding of child behaviour and development.

F. Stimulation of provincial governments to provide better and more adequate facilities for the care and treatment of mental disease and mental deficiency.

G. Provision of special classes for the mentally retarded in the school systems.

H. Establishment of occupational therapy and social service in mental hospitals.

I. Establishment of mental hygiene clinics as part of a programme of prevention.

J. Provision of standard records for mental hospitals.

K. Higher standards and better methods for the selection of immigrants.

The report observed that one notable omission in the tasks so far undertaken was the application of mental hygiene to criminals, courts of law and penal institutions.

Recommendations:

1. That the National Committee promote the training of mental hygiene leaders, and undergraduate instruction for professional workers; and that they give   particular

consideration to instruction to under-graduates in medicine, to nurses and teachers in training, and to physicians and nurses who are preparing for public health work.

2. That the research program be organized on a Canada-wide basis.

3. That the National Committee provide survey and consultant services to official bodies.

4. That the National Committee prepare a provincial program for mental hygiene.

5. That the National Committee promote the establishment of standard records and statistical information on mental illness.

6. That racial studies be made, and consideration given to immigration laws and practices.

7. That the public instruction in mental hygiene be continued.

8. That Parent Education be continued as a research problem.

9. That the National Committee initiate studies of the practical workings of the professions, so as to be in a position to advise the professions - law, medicine, education, etc. - with regard to the practice of mental hygiene principles.

10. That the National Committee study public health services in Canada, particularly as they apply to municipalities and countries, with a view to the inclusion of mental hygiene in public health and the raising of standards of public administration.

11. That the Dominion Government and all the provincial governments be fully informed as to the needs of the National Committee and their financial support enlisted on the basis of services rendered.

12. That the National Committee allocate some portion of the Dominion grant to the Quebec Division.

13. That the relationship between the National Committee and other organizations be, as far as possible, between the offices rather than with individuals.

14. That the National Committee become affiliated with the Canadian Medical Association.[1]

2. Research and Scientific Studies

Research begun in the mid 1920s was continued and expanded. In Toronto this included the work at the Institute of Child Study and the Regal Road studies. The addition of Professor W. Line to the staff of the Department of Psychology, University of Toronto, provided a new emphasis on the scientific method. His interest in a critical evaluation of mental measurement and the educational process led to a global concept of mental hygiene. In September, 1936, Dr. J.D. Griffin, a psychiatrist, was added to the National Committee's full-time staff. He was made Director of Mental Hygiene and Education, a new program division. In preparation for this, he had post-graduate training with Blatz and Line and a two-year Rockefeller travelling scholarship abroad. Griffin and Line developed a special program in the public schools of York Township, then a suburb of Toronto. They also collaborated with Laycock of Saskatchewan in the production of a textbook for teachers on mental hygiene.[2]

In Montreal, the Mental Hygiene Institute continued its work, and in Alberta and Saskatchewan the work of developing a mental health approach in the training of teachers continued.

Marjorie Hiscott Keyes Hincks (1892-1983), 'field worker' and subsequently Administrative Secretary of the Canadian National Committee for Mental Hygiene.

Source: CMHA Collection, QSMHC Archives

Edward Alexander Bott (1887-1974), Professor of Psychology at the
University of Toronto and one of the first Scientific Advisers and
supporters of the Canadian National Committee for Mental Hygiene.

Source: University of Toronto Archives. Dept. of Information Services (A78-
0041)

Dr. William Emet Blatz (1895-1964), founder of the St. George
Nursery School which became the Institute of Child Study, College
of Education, University of Toronto.

Delegates representing six continents attending the First
International Congress on Mental Hygiene, in Washington, 1931
(with Beers centre, and Hincks third from left).

Source: CMHA Collection, QSMHC Archives

3. Insulin Shock Treatment and Banting

Scientific studies were also beginning in many Canadian mental hospitals. The advent of the new treatments (metrazol* and insulin shock) for schizophrenia had aroused interest and even enthusiasm. By the mid 1930s the metrazol treatment was being discontinued in favour of insulin coma. It was felt that the former was frightening and even brutalizing in its impact on the patient, and the results were no better than those with insulin. Insulin was hailed as the long-sought solution to the problem of finding a cure for this type of illness. Yet it was difficult to obtain current information on results being achieved and on the various modifications of the insulin treatment procedures which were being tested. The scientific journals had a backlog of reports which meant long delays in publishing up-to-date information. The time of computerized telecommunication was still many years in the future.

It was decided that the National Committee could be helpful by acting as a sort of Canadian exchange for information regarding this treatment. A bulletin service was established, and frequent short reports of treatment methods and results were sent to all provincial health departments and all mental hospitals. This service continued until 1939, when the outbreak of war brought about a different kind of bulletin service.

The excitement about insulin shock and schizophrenia was very naturally of great interest to Sir Frederick Banting, the discoverer of insulin. With the help of a

---

*A camphor derivative which on being administrated intravenously produced an immediate convulsive seizure. Large doses of insulin produced sleepiness, coma and finally a convulsion.

modest grant from the Scottish Rite Research Fund, the Banting Institute scientists conducted several important studies relating to brain cell metabolism, mental illness, metrazol, and insulin.[3]

Banting and Hincks became close friends, and in 1938 the former was made a member of the Board of Directors. He was constantly intrigued by the mystery and the enigma of mental illness. He visited several mental hospitals and talked with patients and staff. Hincks recalled his comments after these visits.

> "They are going about the job of treatment in the wrong way," he said. "I have come to this conclusion after talking to hundreds of patients and observing the activities and attitudes of doctors and nurses in these hospitals . . . I entered these hospitals assuming the attitude that I was a patient. I kept asking myself if this or that hospital procedure, or this or that attitude on the part of the doctors or nurses, would elevate my morale and self-confidence and self-respect. Otherwise I might not get better. I chatted over these matters with patients themselves who all agreed with the soundness of my point of view. Viewing the hospitals from this angle, I found that the attitude of doctors and nurses to patients was all wrong. They treated the patients as inferiors and not as equals - telling them what to do rather than leading them to self-help, self-respect, and independence. On the other hand, when the patients were by themselves with a minimum of doctor or nurse supervision, they spoke to each other as equals and were really doing a magnificent job therapeutically for one another. The patients, if given a chance, are the real therapists - not the doctors or nurses. You'll have to change the attitudes, the policies and procedures in these hospitals."[4]

The concepts of patients helping each other therapeutically could not be translated into a program promoted by the

National Committee during the Second World War. However, others pursued this idea even before the war came to an end. Maxwell Jones in England began his work on the therapeutic community, and various types of group therapy projects developed and became very popular after the war.

Another one of Banting's ideas was to mobilize a group of Nobel Prize winners in the fields of medicine and medical sciences and, with the support of international corporation executives, attempt to resolve the problem of the cause and treatment of mental illness. He approached several scientists in a preliminary way and even had a meeting with the president and senior executives of the Du Pont Company in Washington, Delaware, but again, before any of these schemes could be formally launched, the war involved him full-time. He died tragically in a plane crash on his way to England in February, 1941.

4. The Provincial Mental Health Services

All the provinces and the mental health hospitals were visited at least once and usually twice a year by senior staff members of the National Committee during the 1930s. Many mental health services were beginning to suffer badly from worsening economic pressures. The Committee's annual reports are the source of the items of interest that follow. Ontario was badly hit. In 1930, a Royal Commission headed by Judge P.D. Ross surveyed all provincial institutions including mental hospitals and jails. All were found badly overcrowded and new capital expenditures amounting to $20 million were recommended. Very little was done. In fact, a "vigorous retrenchment brought about by the exigencies of the financial depression" resulted in even more overcrowding. Many doctors were resigning. There was poor morale and an increase in public complaints. Finally in 1937, Dr. B.T. McGhie, Deputy Minister of Health, with the help of Dr. Hincks arranged for Dr. Samuel Hamilton of the Mental Hospital Survey Division of the American National Committee to conduct another survey. Almost immediately following the survey, a serious complaint was made by a patient admitted to the mental hospital in London. He claimed that he had been mistreated by the Superintendent. Still another Royal Commission was appointed to investigate this and other problems of the mental hospitals. This third survey vindicated the Superintendent and the staff of the London hospital but revealed many of the same difficulties already detailed in the two other surveys. The only major improvements were the construction of a large new mental hospital near St. Thomas, (the premier's constituency), a slight increase in staff salaries and the proclamation in 1938 of a new Mental Health Act originally passed in 1935.

In Prince Edward Island, a disastrous fire in December, 1931, virtually destroyed the Falconwood (mental) Hospital. Plans to rebuild the facility were delayed "through lack of funds" and very modest temporary structures were erected or made available. Several visits by the National Committee staff during the decade and professional personnel loaned by the Government of Ontario helped in the emergency.

Alberta was of particular interest because of its experience with the 1928 Sexual Sterilization Act. The officials and professsional personnel were "generally satisfied" with the results of the 395 operations so far performed! Mental hygiene clinics had been organized in

Edmonton, Calgary, and Lethbridge.

The province of Quebec requested assistance in conducting a survey of its mental health services. In 1939, Dr. Winfred Overholser of St. Elizabeth Hospital in Bethesda, Maryland surveyed the Verdun Protestant Hospital (now the Douglas Hospital). The other institutions, being essentially privately owned by religious orders of nuns were not surveyed at this time, pending further negotiations and funding. It is notable that the reports of the mental health services from all provinces made special mention of the great help and assistance provided by the National Committee and its staff. Particularly singled out for praise were Dr. Hincks, Dr. Fleming, Dr. Farrar, and Dr. Mitchell.

5. Mental Health Statistics

Dr. Harry Spaulding, a lawyer and an expert in the organization of data, who joined the staff, was particularly interested in collecting uniform statistics concerning the mental hospitals and mental patients from all provinces. This work was finally taken over by the Dominion Bureau of Statistics, now Statistics Canada, and for the first time it was possible to compare mental hospital services in all provinces, providing a significant basis upon which to evaluate progress and further improvement.

At the annual meeting in November, 1930, Dr. Hincks presented a report on Hospital Standardization which resulted in a committee being appointed to establish mininum standards for Canadian mental hospitals. It was pointed out that with such guidelines it would be possible to evaluate and compare the operations of mental hospitals across the country. It would be more than thirty years before a Canadian Council on Hospital Accreditation would finally tackle this important task with professional expertise. In the meantime, the Canadian and the American National Committees co-operated with the American College of Surgeons and the American Psychiatric Association to do what they could to provide standard guidelines.*

At the same 1930 meeting, the following resolution was adopted: "Be it resolved that the Canadian National Committee for Mental Hygiene go on record as urging the provision of psychopathic wards in general hospitals of over 500 beds." This also was an idea whose time had not yet come. It was not until the 1960s that nearly all the large general hospitals established psychiatric departments.

---

*The first outline of standards for mental hospitals was published in 1953 by the American Psychiatric Association. It was amended several times during the next years (see also pp 131 and 232).

VII

The Expanding Concept of Mental Hygiene 1930-39

Although the term "mental hygiene" implied a preventive and public health connotation, little emphasis was placed on this aspect in the early days of the Committee. J.S.W. McCullough[1] of the Ontario Department of Health had published a short paper in 1915 in which he stressed the importance of primary prevention, as did W. Smith[2], a psychologist at the University of Toronto, in an article in 1918. Dr. Hincks had always felt that there should be some kind of preventive program so that the ever-increasing numbers of mentally ill patients could be reduced. His interest in this was temporarily overshadowed by the urgent problems presented by the condition of mental hospitals, the seriously retarded, and immigration. Research on the development of children and the training of school teachers were initial steps in the right direction, but it was not till 1931 that he began to see the broader perspective of mental hygiene, a perspective that involved the values, the attitudes, the emotional habits, and life-styles of people everywhere. In this he anticipated, again by many years, the present emphasis on mental and physical fitness.

In his address at the First International Congress on Mental Hygiene, Washington D.C., May 10, 1930, Hincks stated:

> Let us now proceed to a discussion of educational measures that have as their aim the self-application of mental-hygiene principles. It is one thing to secure public approval for facilities and arrangements for the promotion of mental health wherein the actual work is delegated to psychiatrists, psychologists, teachers, social workers and others, but it is quite another matter when public participation is required. During the past twenty years, the practicability of obtaining popular endorsement for mental-hygiene activities in connection with schools, hospitals, clinics and other agencies outside the home, has been well demonstrated. But it must be admitted that the efficacy of public education in so far as its effect upon the mental welfare of the rank and file of the population is concerned, has not been so satisfactorily demonstrated. That there is need for the penetration of mental-hygiene influences into the home and community life is becoming increasingly evident; and educational experiments, therefore, must be prosecuted with vigor to discover possibilities of opening up this rich field.
>
> ★ ★ ★
>
> Much more attention is being given in educational programs to the mental health of the child than to that of the adult. A beginning has been made, however, with university students. In the leading universities in the United States, lectures on mental hygiene are now given and consultation services furnished. Arrangements are provided for the discussion of mental mechanisms - of the ways in which the mind works; of the common problems

confronting students; of healthy ways of meeting difficult life situations, and so on. The general aim is to assist students to know themselves, to accept themselves and to be themselves.

Industrial concerns are not far behind the colleges and a considerable number of enlightened corporations are providing mental-hygiene advice and facilities for their employees who, like the university students and the beneficiaries of parent educational instruction, are thereby not only receiving the direct results of the application of mental-hygiene principles, but also are becoming informed as citizens of the wider significance of these principles.

In an address in Pittsburgh, Pennsylvania, the following year, 1931, he stated:

Within the last year or two it has become evident that mental hygiene must once again extend the spheres of its influence - that it must become concerned with the mental health needs of every man, woman, and child in the community because the truth is becoming obvious that everybody is confronted with mental health problems of one kind or another. This latest phase of mental hygiene concern - the conservation of the mental health of the entire population - may well prove to be one of the most significant ventures in human welfare.

1. The Division on Education and Mental Hygiene

The concept of positive mental health was beginning to take shape. Professor W. Line was a significant leader in developing this concept. In 1936, with Dr. J.D. Griffin, he developed a Division on Education and Mental Hygiene, with the idea that any program for promoting mental health must involve schools and the educative process. The schools provided a setting in which theoretically all children were available for special study and demonstration programs.

The entry into a school system was easily arranged. The Superintendent of Public Schools in York Township, H.A. Griffin, wished to have psychiatric and psychological guidance for his schools. He felt that if some such service were available, even only part-time, it would demonstrate the importance and value of having a full-time guidance clinic. In return, he offered to provide the schools as a setting for the studies on promoting mental health. Line indicated the philosophy behind this program in many published articles. He constantly stressed the importance of teachers' attitudes, their understanding, their willingness to work with children rather than to control them through authority. Discipline as traditionally conceived, he felt, involved a great deal of antagonism between the educator and the educated.

It was decided that the program should have three objectives: service, teacher training, and research. The service and training aspects were quickly and informally arranged. The service aspect offered immediate consultation with teachers, school nurses, and parents, on children with behaviour problems and classroom difficulties. When it was felt necessary to interview the child or administer psychological tests, the principals and the parents were always consulted. Most parents were willing, even eager, to come to the school for informal discussions. Talks and lectures were frequently given at Home and School meetings and to groups of teachers.

As a further project relating to service and training, a textbook for teachers was completed by Line and Griffin in collaboration with Professor Laycock of Saskatoon. The book was widely used throughout Canada for several years.[3] In addition, an American quarterly magazine for teachers and parents called *Understanding the Child* was published in a Canadian edition and achieved good circulation.

Furthermore, an experimental technique having potential for promoting mental health was introduced by Griffin in the senior grades of the public schools. Essentially this was a method of encouraging thoughtful discussion about human behaviour. It had been designed for use in high schools by Professor Alice Keliher of Columbia University. A short excerpt from a film adapted from a commercial Hollywood picture was shown. The picture concerned children and their relationship with other children and adults and lasted about ten minutes. This was followed by an open-ended free discussion concerning the possible motivations, frustrations, and methods of coping with social and personal problems initially suggested by the events in this film. No attempt was made to teach the "right answers" nor to inculcate adult ethical or moral precepts or values. Rather, every effort was made to encourage the children to think through these problems for themselves, rationally and logically; to discuss them with each other, criticize the picture and the ideas of their classmates, and finally to reach a tentative consensus which, however objectionable from the point of view of adult society, was their own. The procedure was referred to as a "Human Relations Class." It was subsequently found that the use of a film was not essential to initiate discussions of this type. After the war the method was an important facet in a major research study by J.R. Seely and others[4], and by implication G.B. Chisholm advocated a similar approach to teaching and relating to children in his famous William Allanson White lectures.[5]

2. Research on Shy Children

Another research project initiated by Griffin, Line, and

Laycock was a study of shy children in public schools. It had been known for many years that the early history of schizophrenic patients often revealed the fact that as children they were noticeably shy, seclusive, pre-occupied and lacking in initiative and energy. It was decided to make a careful survey and analysis of shy children in a large school population in an effort to distinguish those who might later on develop the more serious symptoms of mental illness. Quite independently, D. Ewen Cameron had described the early behaviour characteristics of young people who later developed schizophrenia as reported by relatives. Many of them became irritable especially when being disturbed by adults. They tended to drop their friends and become socially isolated. The term "recessive" was frequently used in describing these pre-psychotic children.[6]

Since the National Committee received a modest grant from the Scottish Rite Masons Research fund for its work on shy children, Dr. Hincks included a reference to it in an address in Chicago, September 23, 1941:

> Prof. Line and Dr. Griffin, of Toronto, with the assistance of Prof. Laycock, of Saskatchewan, made a study of 8,000 school children and discovered that 6.5% were shy, seclusive, persistently timid and recessive in their reactions. It was also found that 70% of these shy children were able to develop a considerable degree of poise, self-confidence, and success in social relationships through educational procedures that included the socializing activities of games, creative activities, and group projects under the direction of capable teachers.
>
> It is felt that this study of shy children has significance to the schizophrenia problem because it has been reported that 40% to 60% of individuals who develop this disability

have demonstrated shyness and timidity during their childhood years and, therefore, efforts that have as their aim the facilitating of wholesome adjustment of such children might have distinct preventive possibilities.

This lead is certainly worth following, and the workers you are subsidizing in Canada are pursuing it with full vigor. Line and Griffin and their co-workers are refining methods for the detection of shy children and for the measurment of their progress. They have devised a social acceptability test wherein judgment concerning the degree to which each child is linking himself up in a wholesome constructive way with his fellow pupils in the classroom is made, not by the teacher, but by the children themselves who compose the group. It is found that children are keener diagnosticians in this regard than are adults. Line and Griffin are also divising school room techniques that foster the socialization of shy children. Line and Griffin have gone on the assumption that, if children, shy or otherwise, gain a better understanding of themselves and of other people, if they are guided in the direction of accepting themselves - of viewing their weaknesses as challenges to develop strengths and not as foci to foster feelings of inferiority - and if children are geared in the direction of helping each other, then a contribution will be made to mental health.[7]

3. Mental Hygiene in an Orthopaedic Setting

As a kind of by-product of this work with school children, another mental hygiene program was designed and put into action by Griffin. He had been loaned by the National Committee for part-time work at the newly established Clinic for Psychological Medicine at the Hospital for Sick Children in Toronto. In 1937 a serious epidemic of poliomyelitis broke out in the province and hundreds of patients, mostly children and young adults, were brought to Toronto for treatment. Nearly three hundred children had some degree of muscle weakness or paralysis which required careful evaluation. The former Grace Hospital on College Street in Toronto was converted into an Orthopaedic Hospital and was quickly filled with patients facing several weeks of retraining and rehabilitation. The place was gloomy and depressing and the children were often frightened and homesick. With the help of occupational therapists and volunteers recruited almost overnight, a vigorous and stimulating program of activities was arranged. As far as possible, the emphasis was on participant activity, not passive amusement. Fortunately, television had not yet been developed. The following extracts from a published article gives some idea of the program:

> The hospital was opened on Monday, September 27th, 1937. During the next ten weeks, 283 children passed through the wards. These children were of all ages from 1 to 18, although nearly half of them were under 6 years of age.
>
> The responsibility for treatment was given to the medical and surgical staffs of the Hospital for Sick Children. It was realized from the beginning that the mental hygiene aspects of the hospital routine were vitally important. Children who are faced with the prospect of lying quite still for months, flat on their backs, perhaps with one or more limbs encased in rigid splints, need special supervision and guidance if they are to develop and maintain healthy attitudes to life and work. Too easily the typical defeatist attitude of the person who is chronically ill intervenes to hinder progress and recovery. Accordingly a mental hygiene programme was carefully prepared in consultation with Dr. Bernard McGhie, Deputy Minister of Health, and Miss H. LeVesconte, Chief Occupational Therapist for the Department of Health. The department engaged four occupational therapy aides and purchased a generous quantity of suitable supplies. In addition to the full-time services of these aides and the part-time services of the psychiatrist, neurologist and psychiatric social worker of the Clinic for Psychological Medicine, Hospital for Sick

Children, there were many volunteer workers who cheerfully donated their time to make an intensive program of activities possible. These included teachers, librarians, and artists from the Children's Art Center of the Toronto Art Gallery.

The first task that confronted these workers was the arranging of the children into groups according to age. In as far as it was possible children with similar disabilities were placed together.

After the children were grouped in this way the task of brightening the rather dark old building began. Cheery, coloured posters were obtained from foreign consulates and travel bureaus, and were fastened on the walls. Brighter lighting was supplied to some of the darkest wards. Within a few days the appearance of the wards was decidedly more cheerful.

In drawing up the programme, it was decided, right at the beginning, to avoid the type of entertainment in which the children are only passively amused. The primary purpose was to equip the children with constructive occupations and creative activities - activities that would not only serve to keep them mentally alert, but would stimulate them to help themselves in many ways.

The program of activities included music, reading, moving pictures, and occupational activities, especially creative work of all kinds, such as drawing and painting, simple group games, story telling, etc.[8]

4. New Immigration Studies

Dr. Grant Fleming persuaded Dr. Helen Reid, an eminent social scientist, to head up a division on immigration in the National Committee. Under her supervision, two major studies were completed and published, one on the Ukranian Canadians (1931) and one on the Japanese Canadians (1939).[9] [10]

In a forward to the Ukrainian study, Dr. Reid wrote:
"What has Mental Hygiene to do with immigration? And why were the Ukrainians singled out for special

observation?"

In reply to these pertinent questions it may be said that the selection of the Ukrainians as the group to be studied was made for the reason that they are to be found in practically every province of the Dominion, and in large numbers in all the larger cities and in the three prairie provinces. Their life in urban, and rural districts thus presents a well-rounded picture of their agricultural and industrial activities. Again, having first entered Canada in the early nineties, they have been here long enough for us to study the effects of the change of habit and environment on two and three generations.

Replying also to the query as to the propriety of the Committee's interest in immigration and racial studies, we consider that the immigrant with a lame or crippled mind is not a healthy immigrant, nor is he a whole man. Canada needs whole men. It is the Committee's function to stress this need on its mental side.

Again, the Committee is properly concerned not only with the positive aspect of the mental health of the immigrant and of all Canadians, but it is also concerned with the prevention of mental disease among our people. Racial studies such as that which we now offer, provide one of the ways by which dangerous tendencies may be traced to their source, and by which forward-looking provisions can be suggested for safeguarding the mental adjustment of the individual and the group. They should provide for the development of a better understanding of the values, cultural and economic, contributed by each race to our Canadian civilisation, and should therefore make for the establishment of better relations between the old and new peoples of Canada.★

★It is of some interest to contrast the purpose of such studies as explained by Dr. Reid in the 1930s with the present more liberal attitudes toward racial recognition and understanding and immigration.

5. Study on Medical Care and Public Health

Closely related to the expanding concept of mental hygiene was another major program which was begun in 1937. The Honourable George Hoadley had been Minister of Health in Alberta for a number of years. He was deeply concerned about the fact that for many people exemplary medical care was simply not available because of its cost. Furthermore, he felt strongly that not nearly enough was being done to prevent disease and particularly to promote good health. The implications for mental illness and mental health were obvious. Worry about the difficulty of obtaining immediate and adequate medical treatment for sickness was one of the causes of poor mental and emotional health.

Dr. Fleming, the Medical Director, had long been interested in the possibility of some form of medical insurance program. Attempts by Hoadley to persuade one of the professional societies, either the Canadian Medical Association or the Canadian Public Health Association, to take on the project were unsuccessful, not through lack of interest but because of lack of funds. Finally, Sir Edward Beatty, the president of the National Committee* and an old friend of Hoadley's, decided that the project was not only important but was well within the terms of reference of the organization. The Dominion Council of Health comprising the deputy ministers or chief executive officers

---

*The legal name of the association had just been changed from the Canadian National Committee for Mental Hygiene to The National Committee for Mental Hygiene (Canada). There was some rumour that this change was made because Sir Edward Beatty, President of the CPR, could not tolerate being president of any organization with a name starting with "The Canadian National..."

of all provincial departments or boards of health plus certain appointed lay representatives approved this action. Beatty quickly found private financial support for the project.

National studies on the provision and cost of medical care in Canada had not been done before. Dr. Harvey Agnew,[11] on behalf of the Canadian Medical Association, had conducted a national survey by questionnaire mailed to all doctors in 1930. About 13% of doctors replied, which was deemed sufficiently satisfactory to draw some general conclusions about the need for better medical services in certain areas and with certain groups. In 1934 the Laura Spelman Memorial of New York invited Dr. Hincks to conduct a national survey and study of public health administration.[12] At that time British Columbia and Alberta were seriously studying the possibility of prepaid or insured medical care. In both provinces official commissions had been appointed to make recommendations and even implement initial experimental medical insurance programs in selected areas. In both provinces, however, the majority of the physicians were opposed to such moves toward "state medicine." In addition, Saskatchewan and Manitoba had established official committees to study the matter, while in Ontario several experimental "health insurance" programs had been started. Obviously the time was ripe for an overall national survey.

Within two years the Hoadley study was ready for publication. The main findings were summarized by Hincks in his report to the National Board in 1939 as follows:

1. The statement is a thoroughly factual document and

indicates strengths and weaknesses of our existing organization in Canada.

2. In connection with weaknesses, the following facts are of significance:

(a) Canada is not adequately served by full-time public health units.

(b) Many rural sections are at a disadvantage as compared with urban centers in reference to arrangements for medical care and hospitalization.

(c) The economic factor creates problems under the present method of organization for the provision of medical care to the middle and low income groups.

(d) The existing arrangements, with lack of equitable distribution of public health services and with the economic factor interfering with the purchase of needed medical services, provide potent reason, probably the most important, for excessive death rates in various parts of the country.

3. The report presents a challenge for future planning to overcome, as far as possible, these serious existing weaknesses.

4. Two lines of progress that would not be controversial are indicated. The extension of full-time public health units is an obvious need. There is also indicated the extension of the municipal physician and municipal hospital plan, to rural areas, plans to be harmonized with preventive services.

5. Arrangements to obviate, as far as possible, the problems created by economic factors in the distribution of medical care for the middle class and low income groups in urban centers are controversial. Solutions that have been voiced lie in the direction of taxation or of insurance or both. The medical profession, possibly life insurance companies, and tax-payers, generally, have views, no doubt, that must be reconciled before the projection of concrete programs.[13] [14]

VIII

The Second
World War
1939-45

1. Special Programs Related to the War

When war was declared in the late summer of 1939, the National Committee, like most of the rest of Canada, was caught without very much in the way of specific plans for useful war-related activities. A glance at what happened in the First World War, with the long delays and confused objections to the introduction of appropriate psychiatric programs for prevention as well as treatment and rehabilitation, led Dr. Hincks and the staff immediately to outline certain important procedures which should be followed.

These could be summarized (as they had been in 1918) under the following headings:

1. The psychiatric and psychological appraisal of new recruits in order to weed out at least the obvious mentally

disordered and hopefully the potentially unstable and retarded.

2. The quick and efficient diagnosis and treatment of psychiatric casualties both during the training period and certainly during active battle conditions.

3. The provision of adequate rehabilitation programs for the return of the soldier, either to military duty or to civilian life.

4. The procurement and training of staff for such a program.

5. General provisions for the protection and enhancement of mental health of the civilian population.

However, once again the government seemed very cautious and reluctant to introduce anything that seemed so innovative. The medical profession, including those involved in the Canadian Medical Corps, were equally conservative and seemed even anti-psychiatric in attitude. Apart from a very well-organized and equipped neurological base hospital,[1] which was sent to England early in the war, there were no military psychiatric installations or services established in Canada. It was expected that the provincial mental hospitals, the hospitals serving the veterans of the last war, and other civilian consultative and treatment services would suffice. The fact that the Canadian forces in England were not involved in actual combat duty for long stretches of time, together with the fact that at home it was taking many months to gear up war-related production, contributed to a feeling akin to a lack of urgency, even a kind of false security.

The staff of the National Committee were

understandably restless. They could not understand why more was not being done. The whole problem had been fully described in the medical histories of First World War.[2] Apart from the one neuropsychiatrist on the establishment of the neurological hospital overseas, there were no vacancies for psychiatrists in any of the military medical establishments. Some of the provincial psychiatrists in their frustration joined the army as battalion or military medical officers. Their psychiatric expertise was quickly put to good use, but they were not granted "specialist status" until the third year of the war. The Air Force was a little more concerned about psychiatric problems and recruited one or two specialists to assist with training. The Navy however was even more conservative than the Army.

The National Committee finally decided to continue the publication of informal bulletins, but instead of being concerned with insulin shock treatment in schizophrenia, the new series dealt with war-time psychiatry. Starting with summaries of studies concerning psychiatric casualities in the first war, these bulletins, "Mental Hygiene and War", quickly moved into psychiatric literature dealing with current war-time conditions in Britain and the Canadian Forces overseas and at home. By 1945 these bulletins were being sent to more than 250 military psychiatrists, psychologists, and medical officers in Canada and overseas.

One psychiatrist, Dr. G.B. Chisholm, who had had a brilliant military career in the first war and between the wars with the militia, was denied a post as a specialist psychiatrist. Because of his determination to serve, he accepted a position as commander of Canadian Military District 2A. He continued to plan for mental health in the Armed Forces and wrote a remarkable little pamphlet on

morale which the National Committee published - *Morale:
A Platoon Commander's Responsibility for the Morale of His
Men*. Thousands of copies of this booklet were distributed
to officers in all services. A letter from Line to Chisholm on
July 4, 1941, gives some idea of the success which this
pamphlet enjoyed:

> It occurs to me that I should mention to you the way in
> which your pamphlet is gobbled up by various military
> districts. Before our recent conversation we had just sent
> sample copies to the various D.O.C.'s, and requests are
> beginning to come in. For instance, we have just received a
> very nice letter from Colonel Grant, Military District 3, in
> which he is most enthusiastic about the pamphlet, and has
> asked for as many copies as we can spare up the number of
> 1600, which represents approximately the number of
> officers in the district. We have sent him 800 immediately,
> and are prepared to send him more if he desires.
>
> General Constantine a couple of days ago asked for
> 500, which he now has. In his letter he mentioned to Dr.
> Hincks in strict confidence that he understood that this
> pamphlet had already been authorized as a text book for
> officers. Since I imagine you were in on this information, I
> do not feel that we are breaking the confidence in
> mentioning it to you.[3]

2. Army Psychological and Psychiatric Problems

Dr. Grant Fleming prepared a blueprint for the
government, setting forth arrangements which should be
made to protect the mental health of the Armed Forces.
This blueprint apparently became lost in the files of
National Defence Headquarters and no copy is now
available. However, through Dr. Chisholm (then Colonel
Chisholm), Dr. Hincks was invited to meet the Adjutant
General, Harry Letson, who asked him what he thought of

the army medical services. Hincks tactfully suggested that "they were not exactly taking full advantage of the lessons learned in the last war in regard to psychological and psychiatric factors."[4]

When Letson asked him whom he would suggest would make a good director of army medical services, he at once suggested Grant Fleming. Apparently Letson checked this suggestion with some of his medical friends and got a negative feedback. Dr. Fleming had been involved in drafting a health insurance program for British Columbia which had been most unpopular with the doctors. It had been postponed because of the war, but feelings were still fairly high against Dr. Fleming. In the meantime it had been estimated that over a thousand Canadian soldiers had already broken down mentally, mostly in Canada, and had been referred for treatment to one or another of the provincial mental hospitals or to one of the hospitals operated by the Department of Pensions and National Health (later to become Department of Veterans Affairs, DVA, hospitals).

The first publication in Canada relating to psychiatric casualties in the armed services appeared in January, 1941. Dr. William Baillie, neurologist of the respected Christie Street Hospital in Toronto, produced a statistical study "A Summary of 200 Neurological and Psychiatric Admissions from the Canadian Army Service Forces."[5]

Another activity of the National Committee relating to the war was the project at Camp Borden in 1941 with the Armoured Vehicle Training Centre commanded by Colonel (later General) F.F. Worthington. He had found that a large proportion of the men assigned to him for training in mechanized and tank warfare were quite unsuitable because of limited intelligence, illiteracy, and lack of mechanical ability. Professor Line and Dr. Griffin were invited to conduct an extensive psychological examination of all officers and men in order to weed out those obviously unfit for this kind of action. Various group tests were used including the Otis and the so called "M" test. The latter test had been developed and standardized by the Canadian Psychological Association 1939-40 in case the armed services instituted some method of psychological screening. Those men whom tests indicated might be of questionable fitness were given short personal psychiatric interviews. And if found to be unsuitable for armoured training were transferred to infantry units. Obviously this was not a popular move with those responsible for infantry training. Nevertheless the project provided excellent experience for developments which followed fairly quickly.

3. Staff Changes and Activities

During the summer of 1941, the Army decided to introduce psychological screening to provide appropriate placement for all new recruits. A Directorate of Personnel Selection was established with Colonel Chisholm as its chief charged with its organization.* He immediately appointed Line as his deputy and Griffin as psychiatrist and liaison officer with the Army Medical Corps. The story of the development of this service both in Canada and overseas has been documented elsewhere.[6] [7]

---

*Chisholm was subsequently promoted to be Director General of Medical Services with the rank of Major General; Line was made Director of Personnel services; Griffin became consultant psychiatrist to General Chisholm.

Line subsequently recruited Harry Spaulding and S.R. Laycock for duties in Personnel Selection which further weakened the National Commitee staff. Laycock, however, became ill and had to return to civilian life, which enabled him to carry out a major study on education for the Committee. To fill the gaps, Hincks made temporary arrrangements whereby Dr. Daniel Blake, a psychiatrist, opened a consulting office at national headquarters in return for part-time services to the committee. Other professional people contributed part-time service as needed.

The Annual Report of the National Committee for 1942 reveals details of other activities related to the war effort.

Conduct of a demonstration of psychiatric social work for the Canadian Army

In November, 1942, the Director General of Medical Services of the Canadian Army requested the National Committee to conduct an experimental demonstration in Military District number 2 concerning the practicability and value of the utilization of psychiatric social workers in the more effective screening of recruits where there was a suspicion of mental or nervous disabilities. In December, 1942, Miss Marjorie Keyes initiated a program affecting men who were enlisting from the City of Toronto. Through contacts with schools, industries, social and health agencies, courts and physicians, she was able to elicit data that were of value to Medical Boards. The next step will involve work throughout the entire Military district. And, if the results prove satisfactory, arrangements will be made by the Medical Service of the Army to appoint social workers in the twelve military districts, with an opportunity for the National Committee to contribute services to the selection and training of personnel.

* * *

Inter-service Conference in Psychiatry

There has been secured the consent of the Directors of Medical Service of the Army, Navy and Air Force for the holding of a conference early in the New Year at the headquarters of the National Committee for Mental Hygiene in Toronto, for the discussion of the psychiatric needs of the armed forces and the Canadian civilian population, in order to arrive at decisions concerning the most profitable utilization of the psychiatrists of the country. There will also be canvassed the experience to date of the Armed Forces in regard to psychiatric problems, the degree of effectiveness of current programs and practices, the possibility of a measure of pooling of psychiatric services between the Army, Navy and Air Force, and civilian Federal and Provincial set-ups.[8]

This was the first of several such inter-service psychiatric conferences. Immediately after the war, the National Committee arranged a series of weekend seminars in Toronto with Dr. Lawrence Kubie of New York on psychiatric and psychosomatic diagnoses and treatment. This was an excellent refresher course for psychiatrists returning to civilan life and was an important factor in leading to the organization of the Canadian Psychiatric Association.

4. Rehabilitation Programs

The annual report contains the following passages on plans for postwar rehabilitation program:

In June, 1944, Colonel William Line, Director of Personnel Selection and Social Sciences for the Canadian Army, approached the National Committee to seek assistance in the setting up and initial financing of a Civilian Advisory Committee to his Directorate - a committee that would convene in Ottawa from time to time and that would direct its attention to problems of a mental hygiene and psychological nature arising in the army with particular reference to questions relating to the rehabilitation of discharged and demobilized men. The National Committee responded to this request immediately; suggesting the composition of the Advisory Committee to include Dr. J.C. Meakins, McGill University; Professor G. Humphery, Queen's University; Professor W.E. Blatz, University of Toronto; and Dr. C.M. Hincks.

With this backing on part of the National Committee, Colonel Line proceeded to secure official authorization from the minister of National Defence for the creation of a Civilian Advisory Committee; and five meetings have been held to date with Major General G. Brock Chisholm acting as Chairman and Dr. J.C. Meakins as Vice Chairman. Plans are being evolved to take advantage of the interval between the date of the capitulation of Germany and the return of our soldiers to Canada to re-gear these men for participation in civilian life. Through lecture courses, discussion groups and individual counselling, our returning men will be motivated to face-up to the challenges of peace in the same vigorous way as they assumed military responsibilities during the war; to be prepared to secure civilian jobs on their merits and not on the theory that their country owes them a living; to undertake home and community responsibilities with a good heart even although initial adjustments may not be easy; and to give Canada in every way the very best that is in them.

Through this Civilian Advisory Committee that is now being financed by the Department of National Defence, it is possible for the National Committee to exert a marked influence on the thinking and planning of military authorities in regard to rehabilitation and other matters affecting the mental health and adjustment of our Canadian soldiers.[9]

It is perhaps worth noting that when the Morganthau Plan was agreed to at the 2nd Quebec Conference (1944) it included a plan not only to de-industrialize Germany but to forbid fraternization of Allied occupation troops with the civilian population. Although this was strongly supported by the Canadian Military Command it was opposed by Line, Chisholm and the Civilian Advisory Committee. Eventually the Committee's views were sent to General McNaughton who by that time was Minister of Defence in Ottawa. He agreed and Canada did not subscribe to this part of the Morganthau Plan.

In spite of these plans for post-war rehabilitation, experience revealed that thousands of servicemen were being discharged with mental and emotional disorders. There were no facilities or special treatment centres to help rehabilitate these men for civilian life. The civilian mental hospitals were not suited for this task. Special hospitals patterned after Mill Hill* in London, England, were needed. The help of the National Committee was sought.

Dr. Hincks found that the Guild of All Arts, a complex of buildings on Scarborough Bluffs just outside Toronto, could be leased. The government proceeded on his recomendation and after enlarging the plant introduced a program designed to assist in the rehabilitation of service personnel with psychiatric disorders. This was placed

---

*Mill Hill was a boys' school converted into a psychiatric hospital primarily intended for civilian casualties resulting from severe air raids. It was actually never fully utilized for this purpose and became a facility for the rehabilitation of armed forces psychiatric casualties. Dr. A.B. Stokes and Dr. Maxwell Jones, both well known to Canadian psychiatrists, served there.

under the direction of the newly organized Department of Veterans Affairs. It was returned to the civilian owners after the war. Similar facilities were developed in other parts of Canada[10]

5. The Canadian Children's Service

Professor E.A. Bott of the Psychology Department, University of Toronto, was sent to England in the Spring of 1941 under the auspices of the National Research Council and the Royal Canadian Air Force. He was invited to make observations concerning personnel problems in the Armed Forces overseas. While in Britain the problems associated with the mass evacuation of children from London and other large centres came to his attention. He discussed the situation with Sir Wilson Jameson, Chief Medical Officer of the Ministry of Health, United Kingdom, and with the Canadian High Commisioner, The Honourable Vincent Massey. Blatz described the subsequent events in a forward to a text especially published for use in England at this time.

> On his return to Canada, Professor Bott suggested to President Cody, of the University of Toronto, that some assistance from Canada might be offered, and so, when Sir Wilson Jameson visited the University of Toronto in the autumn, he invited Dr. C.M. Hincks, the Director of the National Committee for Mental Hygiene of Canada, Professor Stuart Jaffray, of the Department of Social Work of the University of Toronto, and the present writer, (Blatz) to visit Great Britain and determine in what manner assistance might be given. We three travelled to England in the autumn of 1941 and, received with generous hospitality, were given an opportunity to visit Reception Areas, Residential and Day Nurseries, Hostels, Evacuated Areas, etc. Dr. Hincks, after consultation with The Honourable

Vincent Massey, Canadian High Commisioner to Great Britain, suggested that Canadians would welcome an opportunity to help. His offer was graciously accepted, and on his return to Canada he organised the Canadian Children's Service. Three teams of workers were organised and arrived in England during the early summer of 1942: (a) a group of Primary School Teachers who were to work under the auspices of the London County Council in the Infant and Junior Schools in the Metropolitan area; (b) a group of Psychiatric Social Workers who were to assist in the supervision of the children evacuated into the Reception Areas; and (c) a group of Nursery School Teachers recruited from the staff of the University of Toronto and from other Nursery Centres in Canada. This last group consisted of: Miss M.I. Fletcher, Principal of St. George's Nursery School in the Institute for Child Study, University of Toronto; Miss D.A. Millichamp, M.A., Assistant-Director of the Institute; Miss A.L. Harris, B.A., of Windy Ridge Day School, Toronto; Miss Mary Wright, M.A., Protestant Children's Home, Ottawa; Miss Margaret Hincks, M.A., University of Michigan Nursery School; Miss E. Hamilton, Elmwood School, Ottawa; Miss A. Mack, St. George's School, Ottawa; Miss J.Cornish Bowden, Havergal Ladies' College Junior School, Toronto; Miss N. Griffin, Nursery School The Study, Montreal; Mrs. M.McF. Smith, M.A., Manor Road Nursery School, Toronto. The last three acted as Supervisors of the Nursery School Teachers in the Emergency Wartime Nurseries in Birmingham, of which more than 72 were organised. The first three teachers returned to Canada to help with the organisation of the Nursery Schools in Toronto under the War-Emergency Plan. The Nursery School group organised and staffed the training centre at Birmingham for the purpose of preparing, as quickly as possible, the many Child Care Reservists who were needed to staff the Emergency Wartime Nurseries which were already being organised in that community and the Nursery Classes in Birmingham Infant Schools. The writer was privileged to supervise this group of workers.

During our previous visit we had been told that the Birmingham authorities would welcome our help. A brief visit to the city in February 1942; a meeting with a small group of the Education Committee; a visit to several buildings with Mr. W.T. Benslyn, the School Architect, and Mr. R.E. Couses, Assistant-Director of Education, resulted in the choice of Garrison Lane School as the seat of our future activities. The speed with which the decisions were made rather surprised us.

Garrison Lane Nursery Training School opened its doors on July 1st, 1942, to forty-two children between the ages of two and five and forty student Child Care Reservists. We were able to fit our teaching programme into the scheme of training Child Care Reserve personnel already organized. . .[11]

The 1942 Annual Report for The National Committee added these details in connection with the British program:

During 1942, practical steps were taken by the National Committee through the sending of 32 well-trained workers overseas. Included in the group, known as the Canadian Children's Service, were 11 social workers, 11 nursery school teachers, 7 elementary school teachers, a youth specialist and 2 co-ordinators.

The Nursery School teachers are in Birmingham. Under the direction of Dr. Blatz, they organized the Garrison Lane Nursery Training School. This splendid school has already trained over 300 British women for services in wartime nurseries. It is staffed entirely by members of the Canadian Children's Service, with three of the group engaged in the organization and supervision of newly-established wartime nurseries. Garrison Lane is affecting British outlook and policy in regard to the education of "two to fives." It will be a factor in placing the 3000 nursery schools in England on a firm and permanent basis.

The Elementary School Teachers are attached to schools administrated by the London County Council. They are now in London, but they may be sent to Reception Regions in the near future to teach evacuated children.

The Social Workers have been placed in permanent posts in various parts of the British Isles, and in their supervisory services to evacuated children, they are paying particular attention to mental health.

This project organized by the National Committee has been heartily welcomed by The Right Honourable Ernest Brown, Sir Wilson Jameson and Miss Jameson and Miss G.M. Aves, on behalf of the British Ministry of Health; by The Right Honourable R.A. Butler, representing the Board of Education; by Lady Reading, of the Woman's Volunteer Service and Mrs. Massey.[12]

In additon to working in the field of child care, the organization assisted in strengthening the morale of the Canadian Armed Forces stationed in Britain, as the following extract from the 1942 Report indicates.

Upon request of Brigadier Beamant, the National Committee loaned the services of Dr. W.E. Blatz during the months of January and February, 1942, to the Canadian Army Overseas for the conduct of an educational program on morale-building to be directed to army officers. Arrangements were made for Dr. Blatz to lecture to more than 3000 officers stationed in Britain and to discuss morale issues informally with them. He prepared a *precis* on Morale to be utilized as a text in officer-instruction. In his addresses, discussions and publication, Dr. Blatz emphasized the factors that contribute to the building of wholesome morale and indicated practical ways and means in which officers could be effective in promoting esprit de corps, efficiency and mental health.

This contribution of the National Committee was greatly appreciated by the higher command in Britain because of the timeliness of Dr. Blatz's work. He was in

Britain during a period when officers were confronted with the challenge of maintaining high spirits despite military inactivity.

The services in Britain were financed through the establishment of a seperate fund-raising program called the British Children's War Service Fund. This in turn was supported generously by Canadian foundations, industrial and business corporations, churches, schools, and individual subscribers.

By the middle of 1944, Dr. Hincks could report to the National Board that the work in the British project was going well. He stated that of the thirty-two child workers sent overseas, twenty-three were still in Britain. After two years' service, ten more would be returning home while, at the request of the British Government, a child psychiatrist (Dr. Mabel Ross from Buffalo) was being sent over.

6. Civilian Mental Health

While the most visible activities of the Committee were directed toward special projects related to the war and military personnel, the program of basic mental hygiene projects concerned with civilian mental health services and preventive programs in homes and schools proceeded with astonishing vitality. The loss of key staff members to the Armed Services was compensated for by the renewed efforts on the part of professionals physically unable to serve in military posts. It is truly surprising how much was accomplished by Dr. Hincks and his mental hygiene colleagues throughout Canada during these trying times. To mention just a few of the more important activities, they included: a survey of mental hospitals in Western Canada, a study of the mental health climate in schools and classrooms across Canada, the establishment of a National Vocational Guidance Service, collaboration with industry in establishing mental health programs, the establishment of a series of seminars and consultations with social workers employed by Toronto Family and Child Services in an effort to provide in-service training in psychiatric case work and the research on shy children which was continued during the war by Dr. Mary Northway of the University of Toronto.[13]

Extracts from special reports and the Annual Reports of the National Committee illustrate some of the accomplishments of these programs.

(a) Surveys in Western Canada

In September and October 1944, Dr. George H. Stevenson, Professor of Psychiatry, University of Western Ontario and Medical Superintendent of the Ontario Hospital, London, made a survey of the mental hospitals and training schools for mental defectives in the provinces of Manitoba, Saskatchewan, Alberta and British Columbia.

In his report, Dr. Stevenson includes such findings as the following:

(1) All the mental hospitals in western Canada are overcrowded and understaffed.

(2) The proportion of elderly mental patients is steadily increasing in the four western provinces, with the need arising for the provision of more specialized attention to this group.

(3) Institutions for the care of mental defectives are definitely inadequate in all four provinces.

(4) In many particulars there are fine features in western Canada for the welfare of the mentally ill, including attractive hospital buildings.

(5) There is urgent need for the development of higher

standards of nurse education; for the placement of male patients, as well as female, under competent nursing care; and for closer affiliation between the nurses' training schools in mental hospitals with those in general hospitals.

(6) The activities of mental health clinics have been seriously curtailed because of staff shortages due to the war.

(7) Taken as a group, the medical men of western Canada have not developed a great interest in psychosomatic medicine or in psychiatric hospital practice.[14]

(b) Safeguarding Canadian Children

In 1943 Professor S.R. Laycock began a research and survey program concerning the mental health climate in classrooms across the country. This was combined with an intensive education program of public addresses, weekly radio broadcasts, and magazine and press articles. The report of this survey, amounting to 513 pages and several appendices, was never published. Nevertheless, copies exist in several archival libraries and it remains an important reference document. Extracts from this report follow:

> This survey involved an attempt to appraise the degree to which mental hygiene objectives entered into the aims of education in the various provinces as well as the extent to which mental hygiene principles permeated the curriculum, the teaching methods, the behaviour guidance, the recreational guidance, and the vocational guidance practices of the public and high schools. It also involved an attempt to assess how far the methods used in training teachers, the provision made for individual differences in pupils, the kind of supervisory services for schools, the use of teacher aids, and the kind of parent-teacher relationships in existence in Canada, were dominated by a mental hygiene point of view. Provision for the special education of children who deviated

from the average was to be considered as part of the provinces' responsibilities for making adequate provision for the education of *all* children of school age.

★ ★ ★

This was carried out by seeking: (a) the co-operation of the Departments of Education, to have a representative group of public and high school inspectors give their views as to the extent to which mental hygiene principles and practices were in actual use in schools; (b) the co-operation of superintendents of schools in representative Canadian cities in order to discover the nature and extent of mental hygiene practices in the schools of such cities; (c) and by a visit by the investigator to a representative cross-section of Canadian schools with a view to assessing the effect of the teachers' personalities on the behaviour of pupils.

In 1944, 167 representative classrooms in the provinces of Quebec, Ontario, Manitoba, Saskatchewan, Alberta, and British Columbia, were visited. The type of classroom visited varied from that of a large school in Canada's largest city to those found in small cities, fair-sized towns, and villages, as well as the small rural schools of the prairie and of rural Ontario. Teachers were assessed on two scales, (1) Baxter's Rating Scale of Teacher's Personal Effectiveness, and (2) a mental hygiene rating scale specially designed for purposes of this survey.

The survey revealed a very definite interest among department of education officials and superintendents of schools towards a mental hygiene point of view. The implications of the survey are twofold: (1) There must be an extensive education of the public opinion before the public will demand teachers with a mental hygiene point of view and be willing to pay salaries which will ensure getting them. (2) There must be a planned and organized effort to

118

give both teachers-in-training and teachers-in-service reasonably adequate training in mental hygiene principles as applied to education.[15]

(c) The National Vocational Guidance Service

In April 1943, the National Committee secured the part-time services of Mr. Morgan D. Parmenter, of the Ontario College of Education, to extend vocational guidance activities throughout Canada (1) by developing, publishing, stocking and distributing materials necessary in vocational guidance undertakings and (2) by advising and assisting actively in the organization and launching of vocational guidance programs in schools and youth organizations.

> Mr. Parmenter and his associates were eminently successful in their work. Between January 1st, 1944, and November 22nd, 1944, guidance materials to the value of $15,500 were sold at cost to schools and youth organizations. An impetus was given to the development of activities in secondary schools and, since the first of the year, Directors of Guidance have been appointed by Provincial Departments of Education in Ontario, British Columbia, Nova Scotia and Saskatchewan. In Ontario authority was granted by the Minister of Education for guidance activities in all grade IX classes of the province.* Teacher-training colleges and university extension departments have been active in furnishing courses for the training of teachers in guidance techniques.[16]

---

*In 1945 the Ontario government purchased the entire stock of guidance materials and Mr. Parmenter became a full-time director of guidance at the College of Education, continuing the program begun under the aegis of the National Committee.

(d) Mental Health in Industry

The challenge presented by industry to psychiatry and the social sciences had always been of major interest to the National Committee. Now with the servicemen returning to civilian life, the problem of rehabilitation loomed very large. A pamphlet titled *Industry and Rehabilitation* was widely circulated by the Committee, some companies ordering several thousands of copies.[17]

Arrangements were made to grant leave to Dr. Harry Spaulding from military service with the Directorate of Personnel Selection for a few weeks in order to conduct a survey through individual interviews with all the employees of a large Toronto industrial plant. These interviews were based on the procedures used by army examiners in their interviews with soldiers. The results were very revealing and helpful in reorganizing personnel and improving efficiency.

Spaulding subsequently became Personnel Manager of a London, Ontario brewery and Griffin accepted a half-time appointment with a large manufacturing company as Director of Personnel Development, an appointment he held for more than five years.

IX

The Mental Hygiene Consultation Service 1941-50

1. The Toronto Psychiatric Survey

Since the office of the National Committee was located in Toronto, it was natural that Dr. Hincks would be frequently consulted by local social agencies deeply troubled because of the lack of psychiatric clinic facilities. The war had forced most of these clinics to cut back services, while it had produced a great increase in mental health problems for the agencies. There was also a shortage of trained professional staff in the agencies. Many of the workers were willing and dedicated but essentially inexperienced in psychiatric social work and even in modern social casework methods.

In 1941 the Toronto Welfare Council decided that a survey of psychiatric services and the needs of social agencies should be undertaken and the National Committee was requested to take on this project. This was undertaken in 1943 and 1944. The resulting report was a confidential one because of the serious gaps in both skills and services that were revealed. The two major needs highlighted by the survey were the obvious ones already recognized: more psychiatric services in the community and more psychiatric knowledge and skills for social workers in the field.

After the war Dr. Hincks revealed these needs in an address to the Toronto Conference on Social Work. His address was published by the United Welfare Chest. After discussing the various kinds and frequencies of mental health and emotional disorders, Hincks said:

> While the general body of our medical practitioners are slowly becoming more and more competent in diagnosing and in treating nervous cases, nevertheless it must be admitted that the majority of our practitioners have not received sufficient psychiatric training to enable them to furnish a really first class service for this type of patient. There is a need for the strengthening of psychiatric and mental hygiene training in our medical schools, and there is also need for a doubling of the number of consulting specialists in psychiatry in our community -we need at least 40 psychiatric specialists instead of 20. Our existing clinics now furnish little more than a diagnostic service. They are so understaffed with such patient loads, that treatment is apt to be perfunctory.
>
> ★ ★ ★
>
> The social caseworkers and the visiting nurses numbering more than four hundred constitute in a very real sense the mental hygiene shocktroops in Toronto, in intimate contact with the children, the adults and with the families of this city - with unrivalled opportunities to summon medical, psychiatric and psychological assistance to reinforce their own efforts in those cases demanding specialized attention. We have learned from experience that medical men and psychiatrists by themselves cannot commence to deal

adequately with so large a problem of human maladjustments. In the absence of an intimate partnership with these workers, the small body of doctors and psychiatrists are in a position to render professional help to only a small fraction of those requiring it. It is fortunate that you, our social workers, are fully seized with the conviction that your most significant contribution to the community is facilitating the whole mental and social health of your client. It is also fortunate that our social workers appreciate the necessity for their own intensive training in mental hygiene.[1]

He then offered the services of the National Committee to organize a program of in-service training for the social workers.

The Welfare Council agreed with these findings and accepted Dr. Hincks' offer of help. The United Welfare Chest (later the United Appeal), agreed to finance this project. In fact, informal efforts at establishing in-service training had already begun in 1944.

Dr. Daniel Blake and Dr. Ruth Francks, Toronto psychiatrists, both agreed to give time on a regular basis, attending agency case conferences in order to begin in-service training. Institutes, conferences, and seminars were planned to provide further training for social workers.

In January, 1945, a course of lectures was given by Dr. Henry Little, a psychiatrist on the staff of the Pittsburg School of Social Work. Each lecture was followed by a seminar and discussion lead by Mrs. Margaret Davis, a psychiatric social worker who was employed by the Toronto Welfare Council as a consultant. Six sessions were scheduled, attended regularly by more than fifty caseworkers. The response was enthusiastic but it was not always clear whether the growing interest was directed toward achieving better skills in casework, especially psychiatric casework, or whether the principal demand was for better psychiatric clinical resources. There seemed to be some feeling that the enthusiasm of the workers reflected an unrealistic appreciation of the contribution psychiatry could make in solving their many casework problems and somehow it was the fault of the psychiatrists and the mental health services that these problems remained unsolved.

2. The Development of the Toronto Mental Health Clinic

In 1946 a "joint committee on psychiatric resources" representing both the Welfare Council and the National Committee decided that an agency called the Mental Hygiene Consultation Services should be organized, staffed by psychiatrists, a psychiatric social worker, and a psychologist, housed and administered by the National Committee with the object of providing in-service training of agency workers and a limited amount of psychiatric treatment as a demonstration. This joint committee served as an Advisory Committee to this new service. Dr. Brian Bird from the Manitoba Mental Health Service in Winnipeg was employed by the National Committee to act as Clinical Director on a half-time basis. Miss Sylvia Jacobson from the United States was employed full time as a psychiatric social worker. Eventually Miss Reva Potashin was employed as a part-time psychologist.

There followed several years of hard work by the staff, often handicapped by confusion and disagreement in both staff and advisory committee as to the purposes, the policies, and the procedures to be followed. The main problem was an old one: the agency was uncertain whether to stress its role as a consultant and teacher for the in-service training of social workers or its role as a clinic providing dynamic psychotherapy for family and children.

The direction and supervision of the agency was never very clear. In a sense it was a child both of the Toronto Welfare Council and the National Committee. Direction, administration, and financing were provided by the National Committee, but the money required was part of the annual allocation to the National Committee by the Community Chest of which the Welfare Council was the professional and technical arm. The Advisory Committee (originally the "Joint Committee") had representatives from several agencies who were interested in utilizing the agency; but they had different purposes and needs in mind. It met infrequently and seemed to have little influence. The staff of the Consultation Service referred to themselves more and more as a "clinic." To complicate the picture even more, the University of Toronto School of Social Work was expanding its staff and its training facilities in psychiatric casework and it too was interested in the in-service training of social workers.

Under these circumstances it was impossible to maintain staff morale in the agency, and both Dr. Bird and Miss Jacobson resigned in 1947 to accept posts in the United States. Griffin became the Administrative Director, and local practising psychiatrists (Dr. W.A. Hawke and Dr. Ralph Wolfe, among others) offered part-time services. Finally, Dr. Florence Scott was appointed full-time psychiatrist and Miss Shulameth Rhinewine psychiatric social worker. The confusion, not unmixed with bitterness, continued with the agencies demanding services so diverse and varied that the small staff could not possibly cope successfully with the situation.

In January 1950 it was decided that another survey of the Family and Child Services in Toronto, together with the city's psychiatric resources, should be conducted. This time outside resources were used. Dr. Exie Welsch, a child psychiatrist from Cornell University, was the principal surveyor. As a result of this very searching review it was decided to make the Mental Hygiene Consultation Services an independent autonomous agency supported directly by the Community Chest with a full-time staff. In 1952 it became the Toronto Mental Health Clinic under the direction of Dr. Angus Hood and finally the Hincks Treatment Centre with in-patient as well as out-patient facilities for children and adolescents.

The story of the ten years from the time the National Committee planned its survey of psychiatric resources in Toronto in 1941 to the establishment of the Toronto Mental Health Clinic as an autonomous agency with its own Board of Directors is a long and somewhat chaotic one.[2][3] It should be pointed out, however, that the end result was well within the original objectives recommended by the National Committee and the sub-committee on Psychiatric Resources in 1941-43. It is another illustration of a policy frequently enunciated by Dr. Hincks that the National Committee's primary purpose was to survey the facts, make recommendations, initiate model services, and then, as soon as it was practical, place the services with public or voluntary agencies and get on with other innovative projects.

3. Doubt, Confusion, and Change

The difficulties encountered by the Mental Hygiene Consultation Services were symptomatic and in a way reflective of similar difficulties arising in the National

Committee itself in the years immediately following the war. There were many problems.

(a) Dr. Hincks' health was not good. Although since 1939 he had relinquished his post with the U.S. National Committee in order to devote full time to the Canadian Committee, he seemed to have lost some of his usual dynamic, contagious energy and enthusiasm. His spells of anxiety, depression, and apathy were becoming more frequent and more obvious.

(b) The original group of wealthy and influential patrons and board members had dwindled. Originally they were located mostly in Montreal and Toronto, and now an effort was made to recruit new younger members for the National Board from centres across Canada. The new members, however, were unaccustomed to the old pre-war methods of generous personal subscriptions made annually to support the organization. Nor had they experienced the excitement and satisfaction of planning a new and interesting program in a new health field. The country was entering a phase in which the governments were taking more and more responsibility for health and welfare. The potential role of the voluntary association was not clearly understood.

(c) Partly because of these factors it was difficult to raise funds. It was becoming obvious that financial support in the future would have to come from large numbers of people giving modest subscriptions, from the Community Chest, and perhaps from government grants. But these sources had not yet been fully developed.

(d) With the end of the war there was a general relaxation on the part of the public in activity supporting "good causes." It had not yet been possible to stir up much public interest in mental disorders in children, in training more mental health professionals, or in establishing psychiatric clinics. It was not until the 1950s that, stimulated by The Federal Mental Health Grants, training, service and research into the mental hygiene of childhood began to gain momentum.

X

The Mental
Health Grants
1946-52

With the return of Line to the University and Griffin to the organization, an attempt to plan new and worthwhile projects was made. Mr. J.R Seeley, a brilliant young sociologist, was added to the staff. In 1948, Mr. Christian Smith, a journalist from Saskatchewan, also joined the staff with the responsibility for helping to expand, reorganize, and publicize the National Committee. Dr. D. Ewen Cameron* the newly appointed Professor of Psychiatry at

---

*Dr. D. Ewan Cameron became Scientific Advisor to the National Committee in 1946 and the Chairman of the Scientific Planning Committee (SPC) 1951-53. He was an energetic and dynamic person and an aggressive investigator. About the time he retired from the SPC (1954) he began a series of researches financed partly by the Canadian Defence Research Board and partly and indirectly by the CIA of the United States. These studies included treatment procedures which were sometimes used then but would not be approved today. These treatments have aroused considerable controversy recently (1980-88). The CMHA was unaware of this work and was not involved in any way.

McGill volunteered to be the National Scientific Advisor.

Nevertheless, it was Dr. Hincks himself who inspite of failing health during this period brought forward several ideas for programs which were often brilliant, always stimulating, and occasionally the forerunner of institutional services which subsequently have been developed - not always by the National Committee. Some of these are described below:

1. The Mental Health Grants

Hincks felt that the Dominion Government should become more deeply involved in mental health. In 1945 he was asked to advise the Department of National Health and Welfare (formerly the Department of Pensions and National Health) how this might be done. He dismissed this project with merely a mention in his Annual Report to the Board.

> At the request of the Department of National Health and Welfare a comprehensive study was made by the National Committee concerning the type of mental hygiene activities and the amount of subsidy that might come within the range of federal participation in provincial programs. After consultations with representatives of all the provinces, the National Committee recommended an annual Dominion Government grant of $6,250,000 to be appropriated as follows:
>
> $4,000,000 to be given to the provinces on a per capita basis to provide 1/5 of the present cost of mental health services;
>
> $2,000,000 to be granted to the provinces to improve and extend existing services (with particular regard to prevention);
>
> and $250,000 for research and the training of mental hygiene personnel.[1]

In 1948 the Dominion Government announced the National Health Grants which followed fairly closely Dr. Hincks' recommendations and which had an enormous influence on mental health programs throughout Canada but benefited the National Committee only indirectly. These Grants were described to the Board by the Scientific Advisor, Dr. D.E. Cameron, at the 1948 meeting:

> He discussed the implications of the Mental Health Grants for the program and financing of the National Committee. He explained that a Governments Advisory Committee, consisting of the provincial Mental Hygiene Commissioners and the University Professors, had been convened, and had made certain recommendations concerning the priorities for spending this money. The amount was $4,000,000 for this year, increasing next year to $5,000,000 and so on to a maximum of $7,000,000. The emphasis at first was put mainly on training, in order to provide adequate body of qualified personnel in Canada. He felt that the effect, however, would be slow, and that the National Committee would be called on for new tasks of leadership and pioneering because of :his development. He felt this was particularly true in the field of public education. The National Committee must try to look forward to ten years from now, in order to anticipate Canadian needs in this field. Certainly, he felt that the Dominion Grants in no way diminished either the scope of the National Committee, or its importance.[2]

There is no doubt that the inauguration of the National Mental Health Grants played a very significant role not only in improving mental health services throughout Canada but also in providing a great stimulus to the National Committee to become much more active in provincial and local programs.

2. Standards for Mental Hospitals

Hincks had advocated for years some type of rating scale for mental hospitals so that they could be stimulated competitively to meet high standards. In a memo to the Board in 1946, he raised the issue again.

> For 28 years, the National Committee has been "surveying" mental hospitals and has followed the procedure of making confidential reports to the authorities who are responsible for the administration of these instructions. These surveys have resulted in the raising of standards of treatment and care within the limitation of a low per patient per diem cost, (at that time approximately $1.00). Under our present low cost arrangements, the 50,000 mental hospital patients in Canada are deprived of the individual scientific treatment and care to which they should be entitled. It is estimated that our mental hospitals are not utilizing for the benefit of patients more than 25% of the skills and knowledge that modern psychiatry makes available. This situation will get worse unless the public becomes aroused and makes insistent demands that mental hospitals be adequately staffed and financed.
>
> As a means of rousing the public on this vital matter, it is proposed that the National Committee should do the necessary spade work for the "rating" of mental hospitals and then proceed to the putting of the plan into actual operation. The results of rating would be given to the public through the daily press. And it is predicted that few communities, when cognizant of the facts, will rest content with sub-standard hospitals. There are grounds for optimism because of the experience resulting from the rating of general hospitals which led to a marked raising of standards.[3]

The accreditation of mental hospitals by an independent council did not occur until the 1960s.

3. A National Institute for Mental Health

In a previous memo to the Board in 1945, Hincks outlined a plan for a national institute with the emphasis on research and training. He stated:

> At this moment, there is a demand that has been uncovered by our National Committee, a demand for psychiatrists to head up clinics and to participate in general hospital work; for psychologists in clinic and hospital work; for psychiatric social workers; for mental health workers in the fields of industry, public health, social work, education and religion. And, aside from McGill University, there is no bright spot on the horizon for the training of these necessary people - and McGill by itself cannot begin to do the entire training job for the whole Dominion.
>
> This, then is our present situation. How can we meet it? Our staff has been giving consideration to it for several weeks; and this is what we suggest: That a National Institute of Human Behaviour, or of Humanics be set up in affiliation with our National Committee, with McGill University and with the University of Toronto; that this Institute have five divisions, -an industrial division, a division relating to education, one relating to social work, one relating to public health; and one related to religion. The Institute will be concerned only with training and research in regard to the human factor in industry, in social work and in other divisions I have mentioned.
>
> In no way will the Institute duplicate any existing or immediately contemplated work at McGill or at Toronto. It will merely fill in the gaps. It will draw on the best brains of Montreal and Toronto with many staff members holding posts at McGill and at Toronto, as well as on the Institute. There will be an importation, if necessary, of a number of leaders or potential leaders from Britain and other countries. Members of the staff will represent such disciplines as psychiatry, psychology, sociology, anthropology and medicine - disciplines that contribute to an understanding of human behaviour.
>
> For ease of administration, the headquarters of the

William Line (1897-1964), Professor of Psychology at the University of Toronto and staunch supporter and researcher for the National Committee. Became Director of Personnel Selection for Canadian Army during World War II and later President of World Federation for Mental Health.

Source: CMHA Collection, QSMHC Archives

Samuel R. Laycock (1891-1971), Educational Psychologist and later
Dean of the Faculty of Education, University of Saskatchewan. He
conducted extensive surveys and studies of school children for the
National Committee.

Source: CMHA Collection, QSMHC Archives

Canadian Children's Service, comprising nursery school workers, social workers, and teachers. Oraganized by National Committee for overseas assignment to assist Britin's Children Services during World War II, 1942. (Dr. Hincks and Mr. J.W. McConnell of the *Montreal Star* are in the back row).

Source: CMHA Collection, QSMHC Archives

Volunteers from Edmonton arriving in their donated van at OliverProvincial Hospital, about 1956.

(Oliver Provincial Hospital is now called Alberta Hospital, Edmonton)

(Photo: Ernest Goertz)

Source: CMHA Collection, QSMHC Archives

Volunteer workers from Winnipeg leave their bus at the Selkirk Hospital, September, 1959.

(Selkirk Hospital is now called Selkirk Mental Health Centre)

(Photo: Winnipeg Free Press)

Source: CMHA Collection, QSMHC Archives

John D. (Jack) Griffin, General Director of CMHA (1951-1971)
Source: J.D. Griffin Adolescent Centre, Toronto, Ontario

Dr. James Stuart Tyhurst, Chairman of the Committee on Psychiatric Services. The Committee's report *More for the Mind* published in 1963.

(Photo: 1960)

Source: CMHA Collection, QSMHC Archives

The National Scientific Planning Council, meeting, March, 1960.
Clockwise from lower left: R.O.Jones, Halifax; Duncan Macmillan,
Nottingham, England (visitor); Father R. Riendeau, Montreal;
Kenneth Gray, Toronto; Charles Hendry, Toronto; Alex Edmison,
Ottawa; Taylor Statton, Toronto; Frank Coburn, Saskatoon; John R.
Seeley, Toronto; Keith Yonge, Edmonton; Rhodes Chalke, Ottawa;
Heinz Lehmann, Montreal; Charles Roberts, Montreal; Maurice
Demay, Regina; Helen Gemroy, Montreal; F.S. Lawson, Regina;
Clarence Pottle, St. John's; Sol Hirsch, Halifax; Allistair MacLeod,
Montreal; J.R. Beesley, Moncton; N.M. Beck, Charlottetown,; Ed
Johnson, Selkirk; R. Macintosh, Vancouver; Margery King (staff);
Sam Rabinovitch, Montreal; John D. Griffin, Toronto (staff); Back
row at right): Clarence Hincks, Toronto (consultant); William Line
(consultant); Reva Gerstein (staff); Roger Myers, Toronto; Aida
Keyes (staff); George Rohn (staff); Not present in picture): Dr.
Atcheson, C. Laurin, B. McNeel, A.B. Stokes, J. Tyhurst, C.
Birchard, K. Hilliker staff).

Source: CMHA Collection, QSMHC Archives

Formal presentation of *More for the Mind* to Judy LaMarsh,
Minister of Health and Welfare, Chateau Laurier, Ottawa, May 2,
1963. Left to right: Dr. Burdett McNeel, Dr. Charles A. Roberts,
The Hon. Miss LaMarsh, Dr. F.S. Lawson, Dr. J.D. Griffin.

Source: CMHA Collection, QSMHC Archives

Institute will be in the same city as the head office of our
National Committe, but the Institute will be mobile and
will function in Montreal as well as in Toronto. Ultimately,
it will not only be an Institute, but a Dominion Research
Council directed to the human factor in all phases of life.[4]
Unfortunately this plan too was ahead of its time. Dr. D.E.
Cameron, the Scientific Adviser to the Committee, was
non-commital. While the roots of such an idea are easily
found in the writings of 19th century philosophers, and
even in the conceptions of a poet like Walt Whitman and his
friend, the psychiatrist Richard Maurice Bucke of the
Ontario Asylum in London, it was not until the 1948
International Congress on Mental Health held in London,
England, that such a broad approach to the mental health of
a man was clearly perceived and conceptualized. The 1954
International Congress in Toronto further crystallized this
approach.[5]

4. Teacher Training in Mental Health

Some ideas did seem to catch on, however, although not
quite on the scale originally envisaged by Hincks. One was a
plan to provide a year's intensive training in mental health
aspects of the educative process for groups of school
teachers carefully selected from across the country.
Laycock in his 1944 survey had laid the ground work for
such an idea but most of the new planning which emerged
into actual projects were the result of the new staff person
and remarkable innovator, J.R. Seeley. Hincks outlined the
plan to the Board at a meeting on October 17, 1947. He
indicated that a program was needed in terms not only of
prevention but more particularly of the need for developing
positive mental health. A national project was required
which would challenge the interest and enthusiasm of the

public as well as governments. He recounted how he had discovered in Alberta the existence of a prototype for a new profession, a sort of connecting link between the mental hygiene clinic and the teacher in school. He described the work of Mr. MacDougall of the Sturgeon Lake Public Health Unit, north of Edmonton. Mr. MacDougall was a teacher of ten years' successful experience who had obtained twelve months of solid training in child guidance and mental hygiene and was now working as a *liason* officer between the psychiatric clinic and the schools in the district served by the public health unit. He was engaged in discussing problem cases with the teachers, teaching human relations to the children and arranging mental hygiene policy throughout the schools generally.

Hincks described how, on a basis of this prototype, a national plan had been blueprinted by Seeley and had been exposed to the teaching, psychiatric and political groups throughout western Canada and Ontario. In general, the plan had met with great enthusiasm and many constructive suggestions and criticisms had been received which had now been incorporated in the second blueprinting which was now being distributed to all the board members at this meeting. The main features of the plan were as follows:

> A ten-year program which carefully determined steps to be taken each year.
> At the end of ten years it is aimed to have 75 well-established child guidance clinics, 2,000 liason officers of the MacDougall type, making one available to every 25 teachers.
> Every fifth teacher will have three months intensive training in mental hygiene.
> 200 mental hygiene societies organized and operating at the local level, supporting their local, provincial, and

national programs.

One million dollars for research in positive mental hygiene.

To implement this plan would cost finally about 12 million dollars a year, which Hincks suggested could come from four sources: (1) voluntary gifts from the public (25 to 30%); (2) Municipal Governments; (3) Provincial Governments; (4) Federal Government.

Seeley discussed briefly the present cost of mental illnesss. He described how difficult it was to estimate this cost and to sort out factors which had to be taken into consideration when arriving at a gross estimate. In spite of uncertainties, however, it was quite evident that mental illness and disability was costing between a half and three quarters of a billion dollars annually.*

Dr Cameron this time was very supportive. He pointed out the extremely serious situation facing our country because of mental illness and indicated that even if we had ten times the number of trained personnel to cope with this problem, in his opinion, the answer was Hincks' plan. In a way this would set up a new profession, taking advantage of the fact that these liaison officers were already partially trained and could be quickly developed into useful mental hygiene specialists in the schools. Moreover they would be welcomed easily by both the child and the family. He felt that by working in this way it would be possible to reach through the child to parent groups and adults generally.[6]

---

*It should be remembered that this estimate was made in 1947. Today's cost runs to several billions annually,   over one billion per year for the cost of treatment in hospitals alone apart from the cost of absenteeism, private medical care etc. By 1987 the annual cost of all health services in Canada has risen to nearly 50 billion dollars (Statistics Canada). A fair estimate of the psychiatric share of this might be between 10 and 15 billion dollars, without counting such indirect costs such as lost time, disability payments and private therapeutic sessions etc.

Steps were taken immediately to initiate this project. Early in 1948 the Scientific Advisor, Cameron, had organized a Scientific Advisory Committee,(SAC) and one of the first projects this group undertook was to study the details of the Liason Officer plan. Mr. Seeley reported to the Board of Directors on September 30, 1948, the progress that had been made during the year.

He described the steps that had been taken in order to inaugurate the program. These included, first, a general clearing of the project with educators, psychologists and social workers, in order to solicit their support. This was unanimously received.

The second step was the clearing with the political authorities in the various provinces, particularly in the Departments of Health and Education. Hincks received nothing but enthusiastic support from these groups. A third step concerned discussion with the Deputy Ministers and Boards of Education across the country, with reference to the administrative practicability of the plan. Here again an unusual degree of support was received.

In December 1948, a meeting of the Scientific Advisory Committee was convened. After two days of careful study, the Committee had charged, the staff of the National Committee to undertake one, and possibly two, pilot projects in Toronto and Montreal. Immediate steps were taken to implement this plan in Toronto. These included the selection of a suitable community and school system, obtaining permission of the Board of Education, contact with other significant community institutions and groups, the making of a survey of the mental health status of the children in the school system, the organization of a service involving complete clinical as well as consultation assistance to the school system, and finally, after a year or so, a re-survey of the children to determine if any appreciable change had occurred, which might be related to the service. Seeley described how initial contacts with the community, and initial steps in the survey research became caught up in a remarkable manifestation of social action. There was enthusiastic interest and response from all members of the community, including the teachers and children themselves.

As a further step in developing this particular pilot project, Hincks had secured agreement from Boards of Education and educational authorities across Canada, to send at no cost to the National Committee some eleven teachers, to spend a year with us in this pilot project. Seeley described the plans that had been made regarding the training of those teachers, and the close participation which was possible with the University of Toronto through the aid of a Dominion Government grant.[7]

The Montreal project never did materialize owing to new developments in Toronto which required all available staff time. But the Liaison Officer project continued until the mid-1960s by which time eighty teachers representing every province in Canada had spent a year taking academic work at the University of Toronto in Child Study, Psychiatry, Psychology, Social Work, and Education, and gaining practical experience in the applications of mental health principles and research methods in the schools of Metropolitan Toronto.

The aim of the project was to equip the trainees with skills and insights which would increase their value to their school systems through an increased appreciation of the problems which children experience and the behaviour patterns which they exhibit. It was founded on the belief that the school itself, through its regular teachers, could handle *most* childhood problems successfully with a little help from someone with an enriched understanding of children's needs. Such a person would also recognize quickly when medical, psychiatric, psychological, and social resources of the community were needed and could act as a liaison between the school and these resources.

Since this project was experimental and unique in Canada, it was decided after four years to assess the results from both "outside" and "inside" the system. With the assistance of a Carnegie Corporation grant in 1952, Miss Isabel Laird, Associate Professor of Psychology at Queen's University, examined and assessed the work of these Liaison Officers from an outside point of view while Mr. Harold Whitley, a graduate of the course and then a principal of a Toronto public school, examined the results from the inside point of view of the school system. Both evaluations were very encouraging and indicated that wherever these teachers were working they were deeply appreciated.[8]

While these results were far from the original forecasts of Seeley and Hincks, we can say that they again illustrated the policy of the Association, - initiate a new service and having demonstrated its usefulness try to have it carried on by official bodies such as the faculties of education in the universities, the school boards, and so on. The project actually became the responsibility of the Institute of Child Study and continued with occasional assistance from the Association staff.

5. The Forest Hill Village Project

Almost simultaneously with the initiation of the Liaison Officer program, a much larger research and service program was started in the autonomous village of Forest

Hill, then located almost in the centre of Metropolitan Toronto. This was a psycho-social research project on the mental health of a whole community. It developed in 1948 because of the fortuitous confluence of three factors: the interest of the National Committee in the mental health training of teachers; the interest of the Forest Hill Village school system and related parents and teachers in becoming involved in a mental health research project; and the availability of the newly-announced National Mental Health Grants from Ottawa through the provincial government and the University of Toronto for research in community mental health. A description of this project as it developed appeared in several published papers and the final report in a book, *Crestwood Heights*.[9][10] An early paper by Seeley and Griffin stated:

> Like education, the field of mental health has learned to depend on the contribution of many different scientific points of view and methods. It is no longer a medical monopoly. Even the diagnosis and treatment of the mentally ill, to an increasing extent, is a matter of teamwork. The psychiatrist, the clinical psychologist, the social worker, the nurse, the educator, the clergyman co-operate closely to help the patient who has suffered a breakdown in living. In the field of preventive psychiatry or "mental hygiene" the need for a many-sided participation of professions is even more marked. This has always been so since the mental health movement began over forty years ago.
>
> The search for worthwhile methods and opportunities to do preventive work has continued unceasingly. Increasing knowledge about the social and psychological roots of mental and emotional breakdown has drawn attention to *the child*. There is now substantial evidence to support the idea that the child is most likely to achieve good

mental health (and to avoid mental illness) who is able to move from the passive dependent security of early life in the family to the mature security of mutual dependency in adult society. No one seriously denies the fundamental importance of the parents as determiners of the basic living patterns and the foundations of good mental health. And here parent education for mental hygiene is of primary importance. At the same time, it is a fact that only in the schools do we have an opportunity to provide for *all* children the kind of emotional and social climate most likely to help the child develop a healthy personality and character.

At this point, of course, education and mental health come together - the goals are identical and the methods are of interest to both. The possibility of studying what happens to children in school, how they develop their habits of thinking and feeling, their values (professed and actual), their social relations with each other and with adults - the effect of the teacher on children, his personality, his attitudes, his methods of teaching - all this is of primary interest to the mental hygienist as it is to the educationist. And it is the purpose of this article to describe one major effort in Canada where education and mental health are engaged in such a study.

In 1948, Forest Hill Village embarked on a bold experimental demonstration. That experiment has had the support and leadership of the Board of Education, the school staff and administration, and the Home and School Association. It has had the indispensable co-operation of the student body itself. It has had behind it the staff and financial resources of the Canadian Mental Health Association* and the University of Toronto - particularly the Department of Psychology, the Department of

---

*The National Committee for Mental Hygiene (Canada) became the Canadian Mental Health Association in 1950.

Psychiatry, the College of Education, and the School of Social Work. It has used funds provided by the Department of National Health and Welfare of the Canadian Government. It has been observed by the provincial Department of Education, the provincial Department of Health, and by numerous representatives of other institutions in Toronto and far afield. The experience has been shared by a group of teachers drawn from all the provinces. The preliminary thinking, the process, and the product have all been discussed at length with many professional groups from coast to coast.

There are major aspects to this experimental program: a *service* aspect, a *training* aspect and a *research* aspect. The service and training parts of the project are described in this article. In a sense they are all part of the overall research scheme. The discussion of the research *proper*, however, must await the completion of the study and the publication of the data.

The *service* aspect is designed to meet the expressed needs of the school system in connection with the professional mental health services, both therapeutic and preventive in nature. To begin with, this meant the provision of a formal mental health or child guidance clinic comprising the traditional team of psychiatrist, clinical psychologist, psychiatric social worker, and secretary. This has been made available on a full time basis for work in the schools throughout the Department of Psychiatry of the University of Toronto. In a school system in which there are only 2,000 children one might well ask whether a full time clinic of this nature is justifiable. It must be remembered, however, that this is an experiment to see what would happen if an attempt were made to provide relatively generous mental health services according to our present state of knowledge. It is interesting that this clinic has hitherto had no difficulty in keeping fully occupied providing therapy for those children who are showing the early signs of breakdown - in most cases well before the breakdown has become too serious.

The *training* aspect of the experimental program came about in the first instance through the profound conviction on the part of the inter-professional scientific group that an experiment and opportunity of this magnitude must be shared *right from the beginning* with as many teachers as possible. The teachers and staff of the Forest Hill Village schools would undoubtedly learn a great deal as they became involved in the project (in exactly the same way as the researchers hoped to learn), as well as teach the research team what they, as teachers, already knew better, i.e., many of the realities of the teaching situation. But was there any way, it was asked, in which the experience of exploring the mental health opportunities and challenges in the schools could be shared with teachers outside Forest Hill Village? Naturally, it is hoped that the story of the project both in its general descriptive form and in its more technical scientific aspects will come to the attention of teachers through professional journals. But the value of *experiencing* the problems of *research-in-action* would of course then be lost until another similar project was established somewhere else.[11]

The study, in addition to being a sociological assessment of this urban suburb, indicated how the "new belief-makers," the experts in mental health, education, child study etc., while not identified as value teachers, were about as morally effective as the parents. But the project left the individuals of the research team less confident than they had been at first about communicating and teaching mental health information and even less sure of their own personal psychological make-up and their own social position as defined by others. Another impression gained from the study was the difficulty of separating research and therapy in the psycho-social field. On the other hand, the small staff was surprised at how much could be done by so few. Someone has called the study a successful demonstration of community (group) psychotherapy. Many indicated their awareness of a feeling of increased enthusiasm for the community, a sense of collective interest in and support for the project and even a vague sense of improved well-being.

6. Other New Projects

In addition to the research and training activities the staff was involved in other national programs which are worth noting.

(a) The CBC Radio Series "In Search of Ourselves"

Griffin acted as a consultant in the production of a series of dramatic sketches broadcast on national radio illustrating common mental health problems in children and adults. He contributed a short discussion of the principal points to be noted after the play. Throughout Canada, in co-operation with Home and School Associations, listening groups discussed these plays. Printed leaflets to assist in the discussion were distributed widely across the country for use by these groups.

(b) Training Special Groups

Line and Griffin took an active part in courses on mental hygiene to RCMP officers and other police forces, to theological students and clergy (for instance, at Emmanuel College, University of Toronto), to students of social work (at the School of Social Work, University of Toronto), and to representative corporations and industries (Moore Corporation and Bank of Nova Scotia).

(c) A Psychiatric Directory

A biographical directory was prepared of all the physicians engaged in psychiatric practice in Canada and was distributed free of charge to all of them. This apparently routine task turned out to be one of the most important and helpful activities undertaken by the Committee during this period. It was useful in professional referrals, for instance, and was a significant factor in helping to organize the Canadian Psychiatric Association in 1952.

7. The Last Mental Hospital Survey

A major project during this period was a survey of the Hospital for Mental and Nervous Diseases (now the Waterford Hospital), at St. John's, Newfoundland, undertaken by Dr. Hincks and Miss Keyes beginning in October, 1948. As it turned out this was the last major undertaking of the National Committee of this particular kind. Other forms of assessment and accreditation gradually replaced this role of the organization. Once again the surveyors found very serious overcrowding, understaffing, restraint, and antiquated facilities to be the major difficulties. As a result of this survey, renovations and reforms were speeded up, and the institution soon acquired a respectable status.[12]

Not content with reviewing the hospital alone, Dr. Hincks and Miss Keyes surveyed the schools of St. John's and found conditions there very similar to those discovered in the Maritime provinces twenty years previously. There were many children found with severe mental and physical disorders and the provincial welfare services most inadequate. Happily, an attack on these problems was begun almost immediately and was accelerated after Newfoundland became a province of Canada in 1949.

As a footnote to this chapter it should be pointed out that the development of these post-war projects by the National Committee with the gradual diminishing emphasis on mental health surveys clearly illustrate the changing conception of the goals of the mental health movement. The issue was whether to attempt preventive programs which hopefully would promote good mental health or to direct our energies into achieving exemplary treatment and rehabilitation of the mentally ill. This duality of purpose existed from the beginning in the organization and came to a head after the first International Congress in London. It seemed clear that *both* goals were essential.

XI

The London
International Congress
1948

After the war Dr. Hincks was approached by Dr. L.R. Rees of England about the possibility of reactivating the International Committee for Mental Hygiene. A new executive was appointed with Dr. Rees as President. Canadians on the governing board and the executive included Dr. Jonathon Meakins, the president of the Canadian organization, Hincks, Line, and Griffin. The International Committee had sponsored the first two World Congresses (Washington 1930, Paris 1937) and now organized a third to be held in London, England, in 1948. This was most successful.[1]

Professor Line reported to the National Board in 1948 as follows:

> The theme of the conference was "Mental Health and World Citizenship." There were approximately 2500 delegates, representing 60 countries - nearly all the countries this side of the Iron Curtain. The conference

lasted 5 days not counting the preparatory commission which met solidly for the previous 14 days in a rural conference centre - Roffey Park, Sussex.

One of the most significant aspects of the Congress was that no one spoke for himself, but rather each for a group back home, as an individual representing the thinking of that group. All these groups were "multi-disciplinary" - that is, previously created preparatory Commissions, composed of representatives of the various arts and sciences concerned in the field. These had, in the year previous to the Congress, prepared three or four hundred reports, all of which manifested this same multi-disciplinary approach to the problems of human life. The whole tone reflected the thinking of men of goodwill. Attention should be drawn to the unique method of preparation for the conference.[2]

The outcome was the formation of the World Federation for Mental Health, (WFMH) which, it was hoped, would embrace all the social sciences as well as medicine, and which would be advisory to the UN, and its agencies, UNESCO, WHO, etc. The significance of the Congress depended on two things: first whether the United Nations would ask for advice and help (and in view of the presence of Dr. Chisholm in WHO and Dr. Huxley in UNESCO, this seemed likely); and secondly, on whether the delegates could acknowledge the spirit of the multi-disciplinary approach.

A third factor, was the issuing of a report prepared by the International Preparatory Commission, a multi-discipline group meeting in Roffey Park, Sussex, of which Dr. Line was a member. This report represented an attempt to draw together into a single statement the gist of the three or four hundred Preparatory Reports.

"In summary," said Dr. Line, "one came back inspired by the possibilities of coordination of all the disciplines which study man. Mental Health could be a vehicle - if it is not regarded as stemming solely or principally from psychiatry, but from all the disciplines which can make contribution."

The congress, in retrospect, represented the beginning of a great controversy within the mental health movement which had an impact on the objectives and programs of mental health organizations, especially in the West. There were those who continued to feel that the all-important issue was the adequate care and treatment of the mentally disordered. While this was primarily a medical and psychiatric responsibility, other disciplines, such as psychology, sociology, nursing and community volunteer activity, were becoming more and more involved. This was the mental health movement as we had known it up to this time.

While Hincks had developed some projects related to primary prevention in the 1930s, with the London congress, the emphasis clearly began to shift to a much larger frame of reference. The issue was now mankind itself, and the possiblity of promoting man's social as well as his physical and psychological health to the point where he could live happily and creatively at peace with his fellow man. In other words, the objective was no longer directed only to effective and humane treatment of the mentally ill and emotionally disabled, but now became man striving for personal fulfilment and world peace through social, psychological, and physical health as well as a sense of world citizenship.

In the world forum of the 1948 (London) Congress, psychiatrists and the social scientists like Brock Chisholm and Line quickly and happily adopted the new approach. The Roffey Park "Manifesto" set forth this position very clearly. Professor Line circulated the statement of this International Preparatory Commission to the Officers, members of the Board and friends of the National organization. The following excerpts are from this statement.

> The pursuit of mental health cannot but be a part of a system of values. In this Statement, values associated with Western civilisation are, perhaps, implicit in much that is said. Indeed, the very effort to reach a high degree of mental health is, in some respect, an expression of Western cultural achievement. But this by no means implies that mental health as understood in Western countries is in any sense necessarily at variance with the sense in which it is understood in other countries. On the contrary, it may be that here might be found a basis for common human aspiration.
>
> Here it is possible only to indicate the promise which the social sciences and psychiatry hold out to reducing the toll of human waste and suffering and of promoting social well-being. Fulfilment of this promise rests largely on the hope of full co-operation between the social scientist and the administrator, who should be fully aware of the new vistas of human achievement opened up by the social sciences. While far more has to be learnt than is known, it is evident that we stand on the threshold of a new epoch of the science of man, and in the accomplishment of this aim, public opinion, enlightened by a broad system of adult education, has an important part to play.
>
> Systematic exploration of the human mind in health as well as in disease, carried out by psychiatrists and others in recent decades, give some conception of the nature and dimensions of the problems facing mankind to-day. These investigations have revealed the immense possibilities for constructive effort inherent in human societies and the latent goodwill in the individual. They have also helped us to understand how vast destructive forces may be let loose

upon the world, for example, in the form of war, or in the more ominous camps for mass extermination which have outraged humanity; and they point to ways in which such distortions in life may be prevented. Few societies of which we have knowledge are wholly free from distortion of human impulse, sometimes on a large scale, such as racial oppression, or industrial conflict. Furthermore, there is no evidence that the burden of mental disorder is in any way lessened. On the contrary, in some of the countries most advanced industrially, mental disability is more extensive than any other form of disease.

★ ★ ★

The time has come to enlarge the concept of medicine to include mental ills and their systematic prevention. This calls for sustained team work by those who devote themselves to the study of man and society. The application of the principles of psychiatry and the social sciences to human problems has often fallen short of success because of the complex nature of the task and because of the great difficulty of foreseeing the outcome.

The sciences concerned with mental health derive from intensive first-hand studies of human beings and their inter-relationship in various cultures, of normal and abnormal development, of normal groups and institutions, and of pathology of group functioning. They have benefited also from the experience of the physician, the pastor and the teacher, whose findings have been tested by modern methods of investigation and analysis. The field of work from which this detailed knowledge has been acquired include health and social services, education and industry, community organizations, the defence services and public administration.

It is clear that no world-standards of mental health services can be set up since countries differ so much in economic resources and cultural setting. No general standards, universally applicable, can therefore be devised for providing a given number of psychiatric hospitals, clinics, etc., per unit of population. This question is simply part of the whole problem of correctly allocating the effort, and often limited resources, of a community for the common good.

★ ★ ★

There is no room here for an easy optimism. Men's hopes for world peace have been shattered so often in the past, that we would be doing a disservice to humanity if we did not fully recognise the difficulties which must still be overcome. Nor can we take for granted that the insights gained by psychiatrists and social scientists will necessarily be employed in the interests of a world community. Just as the discoveries of the physicist can be used to construct or to destroy, so too the psychological sciences can either contribute to mental health ar they can be exploited to divide and confuse mankind. It is only with a full awareness of these and other obstacles that we can do our work with any prospect of success. There is, however, all the difference between recognising that a task has immense difficulties, and insisting that it is impossible.

This then, as we see it, is the ultimate goal of mental health to help men to live with their fellows in one world.

The fact that men and women everywhere are looking for guidance in world affairs, as well as in dealing with the problems of their own community, constitutes the greatest challenge ever presented to social scientists and psychiatrists.

Two world wars in a single generation, and the possiblity of a much more devastating one in the not distant future, have made clear to everyone the urgency of the crisis. More directly and more clearly than ever before, the question must be faced as to whether survival is possible without adapting human institutions so that men can live together as world citizens in a world community, in which local loyalties are rendered compatible with a wider allegiance to mankind as a whole.

The idea of the "world citizen," as here conceived, is not used in a political sense. It is rather meant to convey the notion of a "common humanity." It does not raise the question of a world political sovereignty, replacing or embracing the sovereignties of existing nations. Such new sovereignty may come, but it is not the concern of this Statement. We are concerned with the attitudes and the ideals of groups of men in relation to one another, and with principles and practices of mental health in relation to a world community.

★ ★ ★

In approaching the question of world citizenship, it is important at all costs to be free from political naïvité. Nor does it advance our thinking merely to repeat earnest aspirations or to give voice to the genuine fears which trouble so many people to-day. Social scientists and psychiatrists must scrutinise with the utmost thoroughness the possibility of using their knowledge and experience in the service of man at this critical moment. They realise, of course, that no contribution would be of much value which did not give full weight to economic and political sources of conflict as well as to psychological considerations.

★ ★ ★

Experimental studies in this field have shown that sometimes friendlier attitudes develop as a result of instruction in schools and colleges dealing with international relations; sometimes after seeing a moving picture in which the members of another nation are sympathetically portrayed; sometimes after contact, on a basis of equality and common interests, with members of another group; sometimes after group discusssion or "group therapy" in which representatives of different national or racial communities give free expression to their doubts and criticisms of one another; sometimes after individual treatment which removes some of the disturbing misconceptions and prejudices. The knowledge represented in these and similar techniques has never been adequately applied on an international scale. It holds great promise. We must be aware, however, that the issue of peace and war are of immediate concern. Methods must be chosen and applied with the time factor in the forefront of our attention.[3]

After the Congress the International Committee for Mental Hygiene unanimously decided to change its name to the World Federation for Mental Health with Dr. Rees its first President and Medical Director and its headquarters in London. The Canadian National Committee was a charter or founding member of the reorganized Federation, and Line became Vice-President and Griffin a member of the executive board.

XII

A Change in Name and Structure 1950

1. A New Symbol

For some time there had been a feeling that the name of the organization was too long and cumbersome. There was dissatisfaction about the centralization of the activities of this so-called *national* voluntary organization in Toronto and Montreal. This was linked with a growing interest of lay people everywhere to become involved and active in the program.

After the war Mr. Harry "Red" Foster, head of an advertising firm, had become deeply interested in the mental health movement. Impressed by the American Army psychiatric film *Shades of Grey*, he felt that the present name, including the use of the term "Mental Hygiene," was no longer appropriate. He proposed a new symbol, the Grey Cross, which would parallel the Red Cross in the field of mental health. He also suggested a new name, the Canadian Grey Cross Society.

This idea was discussed at Board and committee meetings over the next year or two. Finally, it was decided to change the name of the organization from the National Committee of Mental Hygiene, Canada to The Canadian Mental Health Association (CMHA). The symbol would not be a Grey Cross but a White Cross, signifying that although no one had perfect mental health (white), just a very few were completely lacking in all aspects of good mental health (black), still our goal should always be directed toward achieving better mental health for everyone. Dr. Hincks used to speak of our desire to seek the "Iridescent Maximum" of perfection.

2. A New Structure

The new image of the organization began almost immediately to be reflected in a new and growing interest in mental health programs across the country. The next ten years saw new concepts in public education and public relations, in the role and patterns of volunteer services, in the promotion of mental health research, and in world mental health programs.

By the end of 1950, the pattern of change in the organization was clear. Without amending the national constitution or changing the letters patent, the by-laws were extended to allow the change in name and symbol and to provide for the establishment of provincial divisions and local branches. Gradually staff changes and additions were made in order to cope with the new developments. Dr. Reva Gerstein, a psychologist, joined the staff in 1950 to direct public education. In 1952 she became National Director of Program Planning. Dr. Cameron continued as Scientific Advisor and in 1951 organized the Scientific

Planning Committee (SPC). He drew up the Terms of Operation for this committee as follows:

> (a) The Committee to comprise 20 members plus appropriate headquarters staff. Eventually half of the members would be appointed by the anticipated provincial divisions of the Association when they were organized and half appointed by the National Board.
>
> (b) The purpose of the Committee was to develop and submit opinions on all matters relevant to mental health whether these had been referred for opinion by the Board or not.
>
> (c) The headquarters staff was responsible for implementing the recommendations providing always that they conform to the policies established by the Board.
>
> (d) Representatives of the Board, particularly the president, would be expected to attend Scientific Planning Committee meetings as observers and to give advice.
>
> (e) All recommendations requiring an outlay of funds or a change in the Association's policy for their implementation had first to be approved by the Board or the executive committee.
>
> (f) The Scientific Planning Committee would operate through a number of sub-committees meeting prior to the Scientific Planning Committee meetings. These sub-committees would be chaired by members of the Scientific Planning Committee but would co-opt other personnel as necessary.[1]

Under Cameron's chairmanship the committee included mental health professionals from across the country. For the first time medical and psychiatric specialists with senior status in universities or government services began to dominate the scientific planning even though there were some numbers representing psychology and the social sciences. There is no doubt the major interest and thrust of this committee during this decade followed closely the medical model. Of the twenty-two members seventeen were psychiatrists or physicians directly concerned with mental health services, while only two were psychologists and one was a sociologist. Thirty years later the ratio of psychiatrists to non-medical mental health professionals had been reduced to about one in three - a more rational multi-disciplinary representation.

In 1953 the Scientific Planning Committee became the National Scientific Planning Council (NSPC) and in every way was the professional arm of the Association. Dr. Cameron resigned at the end of that year and Dr. D.G. McKerracher, the newly appointed Professor of Psychiatry at the Universiy of Saskatchewan, became Chairman. The chairman changed every two or three years. Their names appear in Appendix B.

The Council was instrumental in extending the program of the Association in many directions. Every major activity of the Association was initially planned at the NSPC with elaboration and implementation worked out by the national staff. A major change of course was the development of the provincial divisions and local or regional branches. Fortunately the mental hygiene organizations in Nova Scotia and New Brunswick had already been active for some time. Both agreed to become an integral part of the new Candian Mental Health Association. It required only their application and formal resolution by the National Board. Other provinces were interested but each felt it had to have a paid executive officer or secretary to organize and administer the division. This would take money. Griffin and Hincks approached the Minister of Health and Welfare, The Honourable Paul Martin, hoping for assistance through the Mental Health Grants. He agreed to approve a grant to one province to assist in the formation of one provincial division. The grant would be an annual one for a period of three years on a diminishing scale. After that the division would have to be self-sustaining. The province of Saskatchewan was chosen because preparatory work had been done there by Laycock and others. At the annual meeting, November 27, 1950, the Board of Directors formally recognized the Saskatchewan Division as the first Provincial Division of the Canadian Mental Health Association to be organized under the new system. Similarly, although no grants were yet available to them, the Nova Scotia Society for Mental Hygiene, and the New Brunswick Mental Hygiene council were recognized as Provincial Divisions as well. A formal bilingual Charter was designed and presented to each new division as it was established.

During the next few years, Griffin devoted most of his time to organizing provincial divisions. By 1960, eight divisions had been established and formally certified by the Board of Directors. Newfoundland and the territories followed later. Two more of the divisions were financed, as Saskatchewan had been, through Mental Health Grants for three year periods. For other divisions "seed money" was obtained from various charitable funds such as the Grant Foundation in the United States.

Mr. J.D. Parks, a former clergyman, joined the staff in 1950 to help develop local branches. He was very successful in this, even organizing mental health committees within other existing organizations such as farm women's groups, home and school associations, church and service groups. These retained some relationship to the CMHA and were called White Cross Units.

In 1952 Dr. Hincks resigned from his long-held post as General Director, and was succeeded by Griffin. The full-time professional staff at the National Office now comprised Griffin, Gerstein, and Parks, with Dr. Hincks and Marjorie Keyes as general consultants. The latter two, with their great knowledge, experience, and personal friendships with key people across the country, provided invaluable assistance. They were also very active in initiating and servicing the local Toronto branch and the Ontario Division. By this time the venerable building at 111 St. George Street was becoming too crowded. The Mental Hygiene Consultation Service (now called the Toronto Mental Health Clinic) moved out, followed by the National Office staff leaving the building to the Ontario Division and the Toronto branch. The National Office moved in 1955 to 732 Spadina Avenue, in 1958 to 11½ Spadina Road, in 1963 to 52 St. Clair Avenue East and finaly in 1973 to 2160 Yonge Street.

In 1955, Mr. Alvin Gamble, a public-relations executive and freelance journalist, joined the staff. His role was to develop the public education program and produce a newsletter or bulletin. Two years later Mr. Edmond Johnstone, formerly personnel manager with one of the Moore Corporation companies, joined the headquarters staff. He provided great strength in financial and personnel administration. Finally, Mr. George Rohn, who had been executive director of the Saskatchewan Division, joined the national staff in 1958 as Director of Program and Field Services.

Professor Line divided his time between the University and the Association. He remained a source of strength and inspiration during this decade. He provided an important link with the World Federation for Mental Health and influenced its policies and programs significantly. By 1950 he had become its president and already was talking of the possibility of holding an International Congresss in Toronto in 1954. He never dropped his interest in research, however, and continued to promote and supervise studies on shy children and mental health aspects of education.

3. Another Proposal for a National Institute

Dr. Hincks was uneasy about the growth of provincial and local programs. He felt these would divert interest, energy, and financial support from the national organization. At the 1950 meeting of the Board, he made one more effort to establish a strong national program which might provide significant leadership and attract major financial support. As in 1945 he proposed the organization of a National Institute for Mental Health but with a different structure. This one would operate as an "autonomous body" within the country's universities. Presumably a major role of the Institute would be consultative, but it would also have promotional and fund-raising responsibilities, especially for research. He was not too clear or specific as to exactly how this would work. The minutes describe his proposal:

> Dr. Hincks then described a pioneering undertaking which would involve the gradual development of a National Institute for Mental Health - an invisible Institute - operating where invited within universities - autonomous within universities - with correlation and stimulation at the National level through an Institute Board that would eventually absorb and replace the present Scientific Planning Council of the CMHA. The CMHA would provide a field staff that would be available to universities for consultation. Dr. Hincks stated that impetus would be given to the national program of the CMHA, to mental hygiene training and research, and to development within

universities of co-ordinated studies of living that may lead to a genuine science of man. He added that, "while a lot is known about atomic energy and the physical world in which we live, this knowledge may be of little avail to us if we do not move forward more rapidly than in the past in gaining insights concerning the intrinsic nature of man living in either peace or war."

Dr. D. Ewen Cameron was invited to open discussion. Dr. Cameron gave a quick resumé of the federal mental health grant picture in regard to training and research. He felt that there was a place for voluntary financing. At present, there is very little research in Canada in the field of mental health. With funds coming in from sources other than government, much needed research would be possible. Dr. Cameron was sure that many of the universities would welcome such a program as outlined and that he, himself, was in favour of it.[2]

It appeared that Cameron's interest was chiefly in the area of procuring funds for research. He was never very enthusiastic about a National Institute, but since it was suggested that the SPC would play a significant role and since he controlled the SPC, he did not raise any objections at this point. In 1952 the idea came up again. This time it took the form of a proposal by the World Federation that a number of International Mental Health Research Institutes be established, the first one to be at McGill University. Cameron was deeply interested in this until he learned that the proposed institute would be directed by the research arm of the World Federation. At this his interest cooled and the International Institute was not established.*

---

*Recently the idea of International Institutes on Mental Health Research have again emerged, this time sponsored by WHO. Several such Institutes are now operative usually in collaboration with WFMH and located at a university-affiliated mental hospital (ie. The Douglas Hospital, Verdun, P.Q.)

Nevertheless, the SPC became increasingly useful and in effect very nearly became the kind of National Institute which Hincks had in mind. The research endeavours of the association, however, ultimately took quite another direction, at least for a number of years.

4. An Expanded National Board

With the organization of provincial divisions, it was necessary to make the National Board more representative. It was decided to appoint two directors nominated by each provincial division, ultimately twenty directors, and to elect fifteen directors at large. This principle of widespread representation has persisted. An innovation was the appointment of an Honorary Board of Directors made up of retired members of the Board who agreed to continue their interest as individuals and provide counsel and advice when such was sought by officers or staff from time to time. There was no limit to the size of this Honorary Board.

During this stage of the organization's development (1950-1960), it was decided that some way should be found to involve not only the provincial members of the National Board but also the provincial boards and staff more intimately in national planning. For this reason, regional meetings of the National Board were planned which really became regional conferences involving large numbers of provincial staff, boards, and local members. These regional conferences were held in the West, involving the four Western provinces and in the East, involving the Atlantic provinces. They were quite successful in helping the members of the provincial divisions and local branches understand the national organization and program and to become personally involved in committee activities. Subsequently, open general annual meetings or conferences of the membership were initiated during which the formal meetings of the National Board of Directors were held. A strengthened and enlarged executive committee now met three times a year between Board meetings. All these helped to consolidate the wide-spread and rapidly-growing Association.

5. New Financial Problems

There was considerable thought given to the role of the divisions and local branches. It was finally realized that although it was desirable to have a strong headquarters or national office and one legal incorporation for the whole organization, there had to be considerable autonomy in the provincial divisions and local branches to enable them to cope with special local and regional problems. The organization, while incorporated nationally, was obviously a voluntary federation. The problem became increasingly clear when the divisions began to approach provincial and local governments for financial support. Immediately they found that it was necessary at least to register with their provincial governments as provincial associations and in most cases to be provincially incorporated.

The difficulty became more acute when financial support of the National Office came under consideration. Following the pattern of certain other large national voluntary health organizations, an elaborate actuarial formula was worked out, establishing each division's fair share of support for the National. For some divisions this posed a very serious difficulty and even an impossible imposition. Obviously, exceptions to the formula had to be made, and this created tension and divisive feelings among the divisions.

The original National Committee, of course, had for

some years been a participant in the United Appeal campaigns in Toronto. As the new divisions became organized, they too entered local confederated campaigns of this kind. The National Office, being a direct continuation of the National Committee, was able to retain a respectable part of the annual allocation from the Toronto United Appeal while sharing it with the Ontario division and the Metropolitan Toronto branch. In addition, the federal government continued its annual grant at the rate of $10,000 per annum. In 1958 this grant was increased to $12,500, in 1960 it became $15,000, in 1966 it rose to $25,000 and in 1977 $39,000. Apart from the sporadic fund-raising efforts and grants for special projects, the national support continued to depend largely on these three sources: the federal grant; provincial division quotas; and, until 1986, allocations from the United (Community) Appeal.

Of course the provincial divisions, when organized, immediately planned their own fund-raising drives. These took various forms. One of the most imaginative was the Ontario project called "Penny Round Up." This began in 1952 and carried on for several years. The idea was conceived originally by Dr. Hincks and was organized by Mrs. Kathleen Hillicker, sister of Marjorie Keyes, with a dedicated group of volunteers. Patients in the mental hospitals of Ontario were persuaded to make small cloth bags about four inches square with draw strings at the top to close them. These were sent out in thousands using carefully-developed mailing lists with a short report about the work of the Association and a request that one penny a week be deposited in the bag and, when it held fifty-two, that it be sent in to the Ontario Division office. Alternately, if it were more convenient, the person was invited to enclose a dollar bill and this would provide a membership for a year. Thousands of dollars and thousands of members were added in this way.

Other provincial divisions tried other equally original and imaginative schemes including, for example, the Manitoba division's idea of a "Make Believe Tea Party." Potential donors and/or members were sent a tea bag (donated by a tea company) and some literature and invited to call three or four friends to come in for a cup of tea and join up by each sending in a dollar.

At the national level there was a great deal of earnest discussion about the feasibility of mounting a "special name" campaign, inviting the larger national corporations to provide substantial donations in order to enable the organization to endow a Mental Health Research Fund. In 1959, a firm of professional fund-raisers was engaged to make a feasibility study of such a campaign. Their findings were moderately encouraging but they advised against an endowment fund. In the end the Board decided against mounting any fund-raising drive at the time.*

Having guided the National organization successfully through these quite extensive changes, Dr. Jonathon C. Meakins retired as president in 1955, succeeded by Mr. J.S.D. Tory, Q.C., who remained in office until 1961.

---

*See chapter XIV, pp 195-96.

XIII

A Decade of Achievement 1950-1960

The records indicate that beginning in 1950 the program initiated by the National Office and the provincial divisions expanded remarkably. New program ideas were always submitted for consideration to the National Scientific Planning Council (NSPC). After approval, practical details were developed by the national staff and circulated to all divisions as suggestions for action. At the National Office it was apparent that the CMHA program could be divided into at least six areas. These were: (1) Public education; (2) Services to the mentally disabled; (3) Survey and social action; (4) Education and training of special groups; (5) Research; and (6) International Liasion. These areas were never mutually exclusive, and many programs involved activities in more than one. An attempt will be made to deal only with those projects that were of major importance, tracing their extension from the National Office to provincial divisions and vice versa.

1. Public Education

While the then national committee had always emphasized the importance of public education, with reorganization and the development of provincial and local offices and the strengthening of National Office staff, it became very active indeed. To begin with, the addition of Gerstein and later, Gamble, to the staff provided a tremendous new impetus. In addition, the SPC (after 1953 the NSPC) throughout the decade had a very active committee, chaired by Dr. Baruch Silverman of Montreal, studying the education program, the effect it was having on changing the attitudes of people, and the way they behaved. It conducted a study of the accomplishments of the Association over the years so the public could have a better grasp of what the issues were and how the Association was coping with them. A brochure on this topic was printed titled *Milestones in Mental Health, 1918-1958*. A brief to the Royal Commission on Broadcasting was prepared in 1956 in which the potential of radio and television for promoting mental health was stressed. A study was conducted on the ways and means of improving the education of parents in order to protect and promote the mental health of infants and children, and a chart was prepared titled *The Mental Health Needs of Children* which was promoted widely on CBC.

The NSPC and staff were assisted from time to time by a group of volunteer experts in the fields of radio, TV, drama, art, photography, and advertising. The National Office produced increasing quantities of literature, pamphlets, study guides and similar material which were distributed either directly to the public or, where possible, through the provincial divisions and local branches. In addition, great use was made of the local press, magazines,

168

and radio

(a) Radio and Television

Following the initial success with the weekly radio plays produced in the series *In Search of Ourselves,* radio was still utilized more and more for plays, discussion panels, and talks. Eventually television programs were introduced and Griffin became a weekly discussant on such topics as Mental Health and Family Relationships.

(b) Films

In addition to radio and TV, documentary films became an important medium for public education. The National Film Board began producing a number of mental health films with titles like, *Depression, Breakdown, Stigma, Shyness in Children,* and *Rehabilitation.* All of them proved useful in promoting discussion and understanding of mental health problems. Certainly American films *The Snake Pit,* and *Out of Darkness,* etc. were also utilized extensively.

(c) Live Theatre

During this period a number of plays on mental health themes were published for production by amateur actors performing before interested lay groups. These were even more successful than the films, for the actors, having portrayed characters in a play, could take part in the discussion afterwards. This method of education continues today.

While these overtures into drama were very useful, they were only a part of the total program. Reading and library lists were issued to all libraries. Pamphlets on various mental health topics were prepared and distributed at minimal cost and a speakers' bureau was maintained.

(d) A Newsletter

A newsletter was published and circulated periodically through the provincial divisions and local branches. This was the successor to the former bulletin and the former newsletter *Mental Health* published in the 1930s. The new publication was called *The CMHA Reporter*. At first it was reproduced on an old-fashioned Gestetner multigraph. Later, in 1957, it was produced commercially with better paper, finally becoming the *Resumé*. This continued until 1963 when it was discontinued temporarily to reappear in 1976 as *Mental Health*. The provincial divisions and even the regional and local branches also began to issue their own newsletters and bulletins.

(e) Mental Health Week

Beginning in 1951, the first week in May was designated Mental Health Week in Canada. The idea had been successfully initiated in the United States and the considerable publicity generated through the press and radio had already benefited Canada. All the divisions and branches joined with the National Office in an effort to obtain maximum public interest and participation. The public was invited to visit the mental hospitals in "Come-See Tours." Schools organized poster and essay contests, and special articles were prepared for publication in the press. The churches were invited to arrange special services and sermons. This project became increasingly effective over the next few years.

2. Services to the Mentally Disabled

(a) Volunteer Services

Soon after the mental hospitals were established in the

various provinces during the 19th and early 20th centuries, the medical superintendents in their annual reports commented on the interest being taken by members of the community in the welfare of the patients. At first this interest took the form of donations of books, musical instruments, pictures, etc. Soon afterwards, however, there were references to picnics, garden fêtes, band concerts, sports day, and other entertainments in all of which volunteers from nearby communities assisted. Volunteer services for the mentally-ill have a long and honourable history. Such services, however, did tend to be sporadic and depended on the enthusiasm of the hospital staff as well as the interest of the public. In the period between the wars and even up to the 1950s, such services seemed to be waning and in some hospitals were altogether lacking.

With the change in name and new perspectives in organization, including the development of provincial divisions and local branches, volunteer programs in the mental hospitals became one of the most important activities of the Association. Saskatchewan Division was a leader in this initiative. Here volunteers began regular visiting at the two major mental hospitals, Weyburn and North Battleford. They found hundreds of patients, many of them elderly, who had been in the hospital for many years. They had had no contact with friends or relatives, no letters, no remembrance on birthdays or Christmas. They were truly the forgotten people. Social visiting and social activities of all kinds were organized. Before long there were a variety of programs and services available for patients, not only in the hospitals but in the community as well. Enthusiasm and interest were high. In the decade of the sixties the volunteer services channelled the energy and time of hundreds of CMHA members.

(b) Social Visiting

The mere presence of someone from home or from "the outside" had an astonishing stimulating and morale-building effect on many patients. This was especially true when the visitor would take time to sit down and really "visit" and try to converse with a patient on a one-to-one basis. For many volunteers this was at first somewhat difficult and even frightening, for they knew little about mental illness and nothing about how to relate to mute or disturbed patients. Training sessions for the volunteers were provided in many centres and the volunteer manuals were widely distributed. With a little practice and familiarity with the hospital surroundings, the volunteers became very skilled in this work and began to introduce a variety of special programs. Often the visiting volunteers had to travel considerable distances to reach isolated institutions, and in several centres (Regina and Saskatoon, for instance) buses were chartered by the Association for this purpose.

Marjorie Keyes Hincks was one of the volunteers, visiting the old hospital at 999 Queen Street West, Toronto. She reported:

> I remember one old lady who was always sitting near the door of the ward when we visited. I always stopped for a few minutes and tried to talk to her. She never said a word in reply and I didn't think she even looked at me. But I persisted and finally after about the sixth or seventh visit, as I passed on down the ward, I heard her state in a loud clear voice, "You've got a different hat on!" It was true. But I didn't think she was paying attention to me. Always after that she talked quite a bit when I visited. The nurses felt she started to improve in other ways too. She went home soon afterwards.[1]

(c) The Forgotten Patient

The patients who had no relatives or friends and no regular visitors or contact with any one outside the hospital were a real challenge. These became the object of a special program for the "forgotten patients." Efforts were made not only to have volunteers visit them regularly but in a way to have them "adopted" by one or two volunteers and remembered on special occasions like birthdays. Sometimes they would be taken out for walks or visits to shops and finally even for weekend visits to the volunteers' homes.

(d) Christmas Gifts

This in turn led to special efforts to remember all patients at Christmas time. Gifts were solicited from the public, giftwrapped, and presented at Christmas parties. The hospital staffs were always co-operative in such programs, and Christmas turkey dinners for all were the rule.

(e) Parties and Entertainments

While special entertainments and special events such as sport days, band concerts, and picnics were certainly not new ideas for mental hospitals, interest in arranging for them constantly had to be revived and stimulated. This was certainly true of the volunteer program. Service clubs were persuaded to visit regularly and organize group games and other activities. Bingo was a great favourite. During a period when games of chance were not legally permitted, and even some churches were getting into difficulties because of cash prizes, one Kiwanis Club member reported the following incident:

> "We went down every Tuesday evening for a Bingo game. We must have had over a hundred male patients taking part

in this with great enthusiasm. We would offer prizes of some kind and on one occasion I announced jokingly that we would have to be careful because we didn't want the police to raid us. One patient at the back got up and shouted, 'That's O.K., sonny, we'll all plead insanity'."

(f) Clothing Centres

When the new tranquilizing drugs were introduced in the mid-1950s, and increasing numbers of patients began to leave the hospital, it became painfully obvious that few of the longer-staying patients had any suitable clothing to wear. This was particularly true of the female patients. Clothing centres were established in quarters provided by the hospital. These were stocked with clothing and accessories, even hats and shoes, collected for the purpose from the public. Some hospitals put on fashion shows with live models wearing some of the outfits available in the shop. The models donated their time, and the whole program became one of festive enthusiasm with the emphasis on preparing for going home. The male patients soon had their clothing "shops" also.

(g) Library and Education Projects

One of the volunteer programs which was greatly appreciated by many was the revitalizing and restocking of the patients' libraries. The majority of hospitals had libraries of some sort, but too often the books available were old and worn out and the selection very limited. Books were collected from public library discards, from publishers, and from private citizens. Magazines were especially popular with patients. Some patients wanted instruction in the English language and other subjects, and the classes for these were arranged.

(h) The White Cross Centres

A natural outcome of volunteer services was the establishment of centres downtown where patients from the hospital could come in to visit during a "day in town." These were usually called "White Cross Centres" and, of course, were important rehabilitation influences. They were equipped with comfortable lounge furniture, games, musical instruments, radio and TV; papers, and magazines were available. Quickly some of the centres began programs of remunerative industrial and creative activity such as simple assembly projects, sorting scrap material, making toys - for all of these there was a modest financial return. Again, such centres were not entirely a new idea. Several of the larger hospitals had developed occupational and industrial therapy workshops through which the patients could realize some monetary return. More usually any profit from the public sale of objects produced was put back into the program for purchasing supplies. But the White Cross Centres were independent of the hospitals and located in places where they could easily be reached by patients who had been discharged and were living in the community.

One of the first of these centres to be established and one of the most successful in the sphere of rehabilitation activity was in Regina, Saskatchewan. Industrial assembly and sorting assignments were obtained from local companies, and groups of former patients met in the centre and earned money, many for the first time in their lives.

By 1958 there were eleven White Cross Centres operating in Canada, all of them involving a number of volunteer staff, but most of them also with professional personnel directing the operation. To many in the NSPC this posed a possible danger. There appeared to be increasing emphasis on output and production rather than on social and recreational rehabilitation. The possibility of the professional supervision becoming more dominant and directive and the volunteers as well as the clients more passive, was a real worry. Also it was apparent that a certain amount of selectivity was exercised in accepting clients, with preference shown for upper and middle-class people who might be expected to be more co-operative and productive. The NSPC felt that this was wrong and that the centres should be "Islands of Social Independence" in an otherwise somewhat threatening and hostile world. It was decided that George Rohn should make a careful field study of these centres.[2] This was done and in 1959 his report was received. In general it was very reassuring, and in consultation with him, the centres developed excellent programs.

3. Survey and Social Action

Critical Survey was a part of the CMHA program in which the NSPC was most active. Cameron had appointed a number of sub-committees on various areas of concern. Some of these produced reports, briefs to governments, or educational pamphlets which were very effective.

(a) Committee on Forensic Psychiatry

This was established as a sub-committee in 1951, with Dr. Kenneth Gray as chairman. It continued as an active committee throughout the decade. Its first project concerned the numbers of insane inmates in federal penitentiaries and those in mental hospital on the so-called Lieutenant-Governor's Warrants. Such warrants, of course, had reference to those charged with a criminal offence who were found to be insane. Because they could not stand trial, they were committed to a special asylum (in Ontario this was located at Penetanguishene and called Oak Ridge) for an indefinite period, "at the pleasure of the Lieutenant-Governor." This meant that many such inmates were kept in asylum custody long after they had recovered from their mental illness. In 1953 a Select Committee of the House of Commons was considering various aspects of the criminal code and other legislation. Dr. Gray's group made strong representations to this committee. The next year Royal Commissions were established to study the law as it referred to Insanity as a Defence in Criminal Cases and Criminal Sexual Psychopaths. Briefs were prepared and presented to these commissions also.

Throughout this period, Dr. Gray was constantly attempting to persuade the government to change the legislation referring to psychiatric matters. For many years words such as "insanity," "idiot," "imbecile," were written into law - words which were no longer used in modern psychiatry. This made it difficult to establish an understanding relationship between psychiatrists and lawyers in the courtroom. The committee also made many efforts to modernize the Immigration Act, which had become hopelessly outdated both in language and in concept. For example, any individual who had ever been a patient in an "asylum," even for a week, was technically barred forever by the existing act from immigrating into Canada. In spite of spirited presentations, the Immigration Act remained unchanged and continued unchanged until

1978 when a new act was passed in an effort to bring the issues up to date. This in turn has been repeatedly debated and amended since, which has gradually improved the human rights of immigrants.

(b) Committee on Industry and Mental Health

This was another committee established in 1952 by Cameron to undertake studies in connection with employment practices and activities at the work place which had mental health significance. Professor Charles Hendry, Director, School of Social Work, University of Toronto, was chairman. In 1953 a large symposium was held involving representatives from government, organized labour, and management, along with the NSPC. This symposium served to establish working relationships with the CMHA which later proved useful. Retirement and pension plans were topics of interest to the committee, and CMHA was urged to study plans whereby workers nearing the age of retirement could be helped to prepare for this important phase of life, without risking emotional and perhaps physical breakdown. As a result, a series of informal evening conferences and demonstrations entitled "The Next Ten Years" were organized in collaboration with Eaton's Department store, for their employees in the appropriate age groups. This idea spread and was repeated with other groups.

In 1955 a Royal Commission on Canada's Economic Prospects was appointed by the federal government with Walter Gordon, a former member of the CMHA Board, as chairman. Line and Griffin presented a brief to the commission in 1956, stressing the importance of promoting and maintaining mental health of the workers if production were to continue at a satisfactory level. The brief made the following recommendations:

> (a) That economic planning for Canada take full account of the need for a concerted and intensified scientific attack upon all existing problems of mental ill-health experienced by individuals, whether hospitalized or not. This means not only improving diagnostic and treatment facilities, but also, and especially, research.
>
> (b) That economic planning for Canada take full account of the inevitable changes attendant upon industrial development both in the social community and in the work situation, by insisting upon as adequate a social science partnership as is now recognized in the realm of physical science. This is more than a public health and sanitation emergent from the bare necessity of industry's existence. It is part and parcel of the development of an industrial civilization. It is far more than a welfare annex to economic progress. It means research and scientific concern, nationally supported and directed, addressed to community living and the work situation alike.
>
> (c) That the important influence of the Commission be brought to bear upon all educational forces in our community which could assist in encouraging and developing the human talents which at present find expression somewhat haphazardly. This means research and action at all levels of education.[3]

It is always difficult to decide whether the presentation of a particular brief by an organization such as ours has much effect on the views of a Commission of Enquiry. A lot depends on the interests and attitudes of the commissioners; in this case the only discernible impact of the brief was one short rather unique paragraph in the final report:

...in considering Canada's economic future we are dealing with the surprising and contrary stuff of human life. The future we speak of will be made up in reality of the fortunes of millions of men and women whose lives are not bound by economic interests nor explicable in terms of economic categories. We speak of labour force for example. But are we really referring to myriad individuals each with his own desires and sufferings and often possessed by singular and special aims.[4]

(c) Committee on Canadian Psychiatric Services
(The Tyhurst Committee)

As early as 1951, Cameron established a special sub-committee of the (then) Scientific Planning Committee to study various aspects of Canadian psychiatry in the light of rapidly changing social conditions. Dr. A.B. Stokes of Toronto was chairman. One of the first tasks undertaken was to review the various prepaid medical service plans (Associated Medical Services, Blue Cross, etc.) in order to determine the adequacy with which the psychiatric therapy was covered. Serious limitations were found in all such plans.

In 1952 a survey of seven provinces was made to determine the extent to which psychiatric facilities and services were being provided by general hospitals. It was found that there were practically no services of this kind in those general hospitals located in small towns or rural areas, and only eleven general hospitals in the larger centres had such facilities. It was discovered that there were virtually no specially-designed psychiatric hospitals for children or for the aged. It was estimated that the provincial mental hospitals were overcrowded by at least 70 per cent.

Dr. McKerracher, as the new chairman of the NSPC, decided in 1954 that an intensive effort should be made to study the whole organization of psychiatric services in depth. Dr. James Tyhurst, the newly appointed Professor of Psychiatry at University of British Columbia, was made chairman and Robert J. Weil, Ab Hoffer, and C.A. Roberts joined the committee. A start was made by studying the situation in Nova Scotia and Saskatchewan. In 1955 the committee was substantially strengthened. S. Lawson had become the Director of Psychiatric Services for Saskatchewan, so he replaced Hoffer. Burdett McNeel and Rhodes Chalke from Ontario and C.C. Taylor from Quebec were added.

The terms of reference of this committee were then made more explicit:

(1) to examine the existing mental health services in Canada; to explore and describe the existing patterns of care, and the reasons why these patterns had developed the way they had; and, especially, to find and expose the gaps in existing services; and (2) to devise fundamental new and more adequate patterns of diagnosis, treatment, care and prevention; and to initiate a trend, if possible, towards the changes in mental health services such innovations would create. In short, it was felt that merely to strive for more money, more services,more staff, and better conditions within the existing patterns of care was not enough; nothing short of a radical new concept of treatment and care was needed.

The committee met frequently over a period of five years. Although all the members were psychiatrists, consultants from the other mental health disciplines were constantly invited to the meetings and were deeply involved. Draft interim reports were prepared and widely circulated. Feedback was extensive, critical and very helpful. A further review was provided by the Second

Canadian Institute on Mental Health Services sponsored by the Canadian Psychiatric Association in 1961. By 1963 the final report was completed and published.[5]

Among the obvious inadequacies in psychiatric services at that time were the following: 1. The large, isolated, overcrowded and understaffed mental hospitals, controlled by a centralized provincial beaurocracy; 2. the lack of co-ordinated after-care and rehabilitation programs; 3. insufficient number and limited range of community psychiatric services; 4. personnel shortage in all fields; and 5. government Acts and Regulations which seemed to overstress the legal formalities of admission and treatment and, at the same time, denied mental patients the rights available for patients suffering from physical illness. In other words, the pattern of services for the mentally ill was basically different administratively, legally, financially, medically and even socially from those suffering from physical illness.

The committee's recommendations were summarized by Griffin at the annual meeting of the American Psychiatric Association in Los Angeles in May 1964 and appeared in the journal of the association the following November.[6]

> The keynote of all recommendations made in the final report is that *mental illness should be dealt with in the same organizational, administrative, and professional framework as physical illness.* It is believed that only in this way will a patient suffering from mental illness receive the same excellence of medical care and ancillary health services as quickly, easily and efficiently as the patient suffering from physical illness.
>
> An important corollary to this basic principle is that any plan, "national, provincial or local, designed to afford

financial protection against the cost of preventive measures, diagnosis and treatment by physicians and other professional health personnel in office, clinic or hospital or against cost of convalescent care, rehabilitation and drugs, should apply without distinction to mental as to physical illness."

In developing this theme, the committee accepted an idiom devised by one of its members and which came to be known as the "McNeel Ideal." This states that the patient's life should be disrupted by psychiatric treatment as little as possible. Psychiatric services should be located where they may care for the patient; (a) without loss of his job; but, if that is necessary; (b) without his leaving home; but, if that is necessary; (c) without leaving the community; but, if that is necessary; (d) without loss of his community ties and relationships.

This theme has been spelled out in five major principles and 57 detailed recommendations. The major propositions are as follows:

1. *That psychiatric services be integrated with the physical and personnel resources of the rest of medicine.* The separation of the mental hospital from other medical services in Canada in the past has contributed to the idea that the psychiatric patient is not a medical patient. It was felt that the central role of the family doctor in case finding, early treatment, and his use of consulation and referral procedures should be emphasized. Psychiatric services in close relation to, or as an integral part of, general hospitals are helping to implement this recommendation.

2. *That a wide range of psychiatric services be established in centres of population on a regional basis.* This is the familiar principle of comprehensive community psychiatric treatment services so urgently demanded by the late President John F. Kennedy of the United States and requires no further elaboration here.

3. *That the management and administration of psychiatric services be decentralized.* This implies that the provincial governments should gradually relinquish the control and administration of mental hospitals. These should be reconstituted in the same organizational pattern as our general hospitals with local corporate boards of management and financed under the same hospital insurance plan as general hospitals. When administrative decisions are made locally on the basis of local needs, concern and responsibility are fostered in the community and local involvement is encouraged. Administrative decentralization permits the necessary flexibility and adaptability in planning appropriate services.

4. *That patients should receive appropriate professional help in their community through all phases of their illness without interruption.* This implies professional staffs, adequate in numbers and training, working in close co-operation within a closely-knit system of psychiatric services. It is closely related to the last major principle, which is:

5. *That local psychiatric services in hospitals, clinics, and other services and agencies be co-ordinated to promote maximum effectiveness (the principle of continuity of care).* Such co-ordination is necessary to prevent the development of gaps and overlaps, and to avoid waste of professional time caused by patients "shopping around." It also promotes the development of special interests and competencies in various facilities.

It is of some interest that almost simultaneously with the work and the report of this committee, a Joint Commission was established by Act of Congress in the United States. Its report "Action for Mental Health"[7] appeared just a year before that of the Canadian Committee. While there were many areas of agreement, there were also areas of difference in emphasis and even disagreement in principle. One major difference was the total cost of these two projects. It was calculated that the total cost of the Canadian committee's seven years of hard work was approximatelly $37,000. Most of this support was provided by the Millbank and Commonwealth Funds and some pharmaceutical firms. The total cost of the American Joint Commission is estimated at well over 1.5 million dollars.

As by-products of the work of this committee, several briefs were prepared for presentation to the government or to Royal Commissions. The first of these stressed the importance of including mental hospitals in any national plan for hospital insurance. It was presented to the Department of National Health and Welfare in 1955. Two years later, when the government announced its plan, the mental hospitals were omitted. A vigorous protest was launched but it was argued that these hospitals were supported by the provincial governments and therefore did not need any federal assistance. However, a concession was made to include the psychiatric units in general hospitals in the insurance plan. This was a partial victory.

In 1956 both Saskatchewan and Nova Scotia Divisions of CMHA submitted briefs to their respective governments. Saskatchewan's brief urged the establishment of small regional hospitals to replace the large isolated institutions now in use. Nova Scotia's brief concerned the management of the Cape Breton Hospital, which had come under public criticism because of alleged mistreatment of mentally-ill patients.

In May 1962 a substantial brief was presented to the Royal Commission on Health Services led by Dr. G. Emmett Hall.[8] This brief covered most of the recommendations published in the Tyhurst Committee's final report , 1963. Some of the principal recommendations

Dr. Robert O. Jones and Dr. Burdett McNeel with Judge Ian Dubianski, president of the CMHA, discussing the program of the joint conference of the CMHA and the Canadian Medical Association on 'Medical Action for Mental Health', March 1964.

Source: CMHA Collection, QSMHC Archives

Mrs. Marjorie Keyes Hincks and Dr. John D. Griffin present a
portrait of Dr. Hincks to Dr. Reva Gerstein, Chairman of the Board
of the new Hincks Treatment Centre, Toronto, January 20, 1967.

Source: CMHA Collection, QSMHC Archives

Formal presentation of *The Law and Mental Disorder* to John Turner,
Minister of Justice, 1969. Left to right: Mr. Brian Crane, Dr. Rhodes
Chalke, the Hon. Mr. John Turner.

George Rohn, General Director from 1971 to 1987, of the Canadian
Mental Health Association.

Source: CMHA Collection, QSMHC Archives

were also reflected in federal legislation at this time concerning health insurance. Dr. C.A. Roberts summarized these acts as follows:

> The introduction of universally available hospital insurance (1957), with federal assistance but administered and organized by the provinces, had a major impact on the development of psychiatric care, but in the face of very widely developed and co-ordinated pressures, the federal government modified its position so that only the provincial mental hospitals and other services traditionally provided and financed by the provinces were excluded. This had a powerful impact in future developments in Canada. As there was about fifty percent federal sharing in the cost of general hospital services we witnessed a continuing and widespread development of comprehensive psychiatric services based on the general hospitals. The mental hospitals have had their ups and downs since that time. In general their significance in the overall mental health program has diminished, the resident population has decreased and most of them are no longer in a position to act as regional centres for comprehensive mental health services. More important, as an increasing but not clearly defined proportion of government expenditures for mental health was provided through the hospital insurance program, this program began to play an ever-greater part in the organization, development and administration of psychiatric services. Furthermore, these developments contributed to a decreasing significance in the role of the provincial mental health divisions in the Ministeries of Health across Canada.

★ ★ ★

The introduction of universal medical care with no exclusions some ten years later (1967) fostered the same pattern of integrated care. Psychiatrists and patients in need of psychiatric treatment are now accorded the same privileges and controls under the universal medical program as are all other psysicians and their patients.[9]

4. Education and Training of Special Groups

After the war the universities had quickly organized postgraduate training programs for psychiatrists, clinical psychologists, and psychiatric social workers in an effort to correct the serious lack of professional mental health workers. The National Office of the Association therefore turned its attention to other professional groups that had contributions to make in this field but which seemed in danger of being neglected.

(a) Teachers

Mention has already been made of the selection and training of teachers in mental health (the Liason Officer Project) and this project continued well into the 1960s under the supervision of the Institute of Child Study at the University of Toronto. By 1962 some eighty teachers had been trained in this one-year course. The project had attracted international attention, and six teachers from Thailand were sent by their government for training. Line and Dr. King returned to Thailand with them after they had completed their training and helped them to establish an Institute for Child Study and Education in that country.

By the 1960s, other universities and provincial educational systems had begun to introduce similar programs of their own in teacher training. The NSPC decided to undertake a study of the leading teacher training colleges, faculties of education, and normal schools across the country to see what was now being taught in the way of mental health. This was carried out by S.R. Laycock. He reported the results as being satisfactory. Most of the institutions were increasing the mental health, psychological, and social science content of their curricula significantly.

In 1968 a second evaluation of the project was carried out by Mr. Alex Sim in preparation for a seminar in memory of Professor Line who died in 1964. This report was a theoretical reappraisal of this research area and in contrast to previous reports somewhat negative in its findings. The following are extracts from this report:

> A demonstration carried on with too much publicity and too little research in one place soon becomes a programmatic cliché endlessly repeated elsewhere long after the creative impulses which animate the pilot project are lost or forgotten.

★ ★ ★

> The choice of the school as a fulcrum upon which to effect massive social change now appears to have been unfruitful strategy. This is not to single out the school especially as a big organization, impervious to change through its massiveness, growing power and increasing unwieldiness, to offer strong argument for choosing a more vulnerable point of access. The school indeed is constantly changing but the impulses come from internal assessment dictated by the need for administrative comfort more than they do from the difficulty the school has had in meeting the needs of children.

★ ★ ★

> The strategy of retraining teachers to bring about changes in the school was undoubtedly too optimistic and therefore unrealistic. We already know too much about the resistance of big organizations to change and reform to believe a professional group which has created the organization can effect fundamental changes in its functions. A change agent

> must come from the outside because he asks unfamiliar questions; because he finds strengths and weaknesses in unexpected places totally unsuspected by the workers inside. If change agents are not to be admitted to the school unless they have five or ten years' experience in the classroom, as many respondents to the questionnaire stipulated, we must read from this that the school is not ready for self-assessment and not ready to analyze its failures.[10]

Subsequent experience suggests that changes in the educational process are indeed slow and the challenge of establishing a sound mental hygiene attitude in the schools still exists.

(b) Nurses

In 1952 the SPC became concerned about the training of nurses in psychiatry. Marjorie Keyes and Reva Gerstein conducted a survey of the nature and extent of education in this field then available in the larger schools of Nursing. It quickly became obvious that courses leading to certification as a Registered Nurse were seriously lacking in instruction and experience in the field of mental health. In addition, there was very little interest displayed by the nurses-in-training or by recent graduates in pursuing a career in psychiatric nursing. The reasons offered were mostly related to lack of opportunity for advancement, lack of encouraging therapeutic results, and lack of any real knowledge about psychiatry. In discussion with the Canadian Nursing Association and with Directors of the Training Schools, it was evident that there was great interest in suggestions concerning curricula changes which would provide training and experience in this field.

A model curriculum for a course in psychiatric nursing was drawn up and circulated to all training schools, including those in mental hospitals. It was recommended that a three months' affiliation for all nurses in the R.N. courses be provided in accredited psychiatric centres. In 1954, after a presentation by the Medical Officer of Health (MOH) for Toronto, Dr. L.A. Pequegnat, it was proposed that the public health nurses be given special training in the mental health aspects of mother-child relationships and preventive or mental hygiene techniques applicable in the community. Action on this proposal was delayed by the advent of the 1954 International Congress, but by 1956 Dr. Margery King and Professor Line were busy establishing discussion groups and lectures for groups of public health nurses employed in the Toronto area. The MOH was very satisfied with the results. Similar training sessions were continued using the Department of Health's staff resources.

(c) Clergy

By the late 1950s there was increasing interest among the clergy in mental and emotional health. Requests for mental health workshops were being received and consultations with the clergy on subject matter, techniques of counselling, and the role of the church generally in community mental health were frequent. Laycock had produced a book on Pastoral Counselling which was published under the aegis of the CMHA. This was proving to be very useful.

XIV

An Experiment in Research Support (1957-67)

An interest in research and an awareness of the necessity of expanding our knowledge about the causes and treatment of mental disorders and, even more important, of the methods of the primary prevention of such disorders and the promotion of good or positive mental health have consistently been present in the aims and objects of the Association since its founding in 1918. The work of Bott and Blatz in Toronto and of Mitchell and Silverman in Montreal in the 1920s represented a determined effort in this direction. The studies of Line and Griffin in the 1930s on shy children was another. This latter project was continued through the war years by Dr. Mary Northway of the Institute of Child Study, University of Toronto. Other studies followed, including the Forest Hill Village Research, and a study sponsored by the CBC on the radio-listening habits of children. It was felt that radio dramas and news stories involving violence and criminal behaviour were listened to perhaps too avidly by children and were having a deleterious effect on their behaviour, possibly an important cause of the notable increase in delinquency. The study involved 4,000 children in nine cities. However it revealed little difference between the listening habits of delinquent and non-delinquent children. The issue of the impact of such programs at this time remained a matter of opinion rather than fact.

Another study undertaken in the 1950s was in collaboration with an international project on mental health factors in the admission, care, and treatment of physically sick people in general hospitals, in the way in which small children were prepared for admission to hospitals and in mental hygiene aspects of their nursing and medical care. The experience which Griffin had in the orthopedic hospital with the young victims of the 1937 polio epidemic was useful here. In this study there was close collaboration with the Canadian Paediatric Society and other groups interested in children.

When the NSPC finally began to take a serious look at research planning and financing in 1955, the first thought was to try to influence the Medical Research Council to devote more attention and money to the field of psychiatry and mental health. But the national mental health grants were a confusing factor. The federal government expected the provincial governments to promote and jointly finance such work. The departments of psychology and psychiatry in the various universities were seriously interested in obtaining research funds but applications had to be made and approved for each specific project and the administrative problems were considerable. It was clear that a new and different kind of approach to the stimulation and funding of mental health research was needed. A committee was appointed in 1957 to study the problem and if possible arrive at a recommendation for a unique National Mental Health Research Fund which would be supported by the Canadian Mental Health Association across the country.

This ad hoc committee comprised the following: Dr. A.B. Stokes, (Chairman), Mr. John R. Seeley, Prof. Roger Myers, Prof. W. Line, Dr. Heinz Lehmann (corresponding member), Dr. Burdett McNeel and Dr. J.D. Griffin (ex officio). This committee met in May 1957 and a report was submitted to the NSPC and then to the National Board of Directors at its Annual Meeting in Toronto, June, 1957. In summary it stated that until 1948, research in the mental health field was insignificant except for projects privately financed in certain of the larger universities and occasional projects conducted by the CMHA itself and by a few of the mental hospitals. With the advent of the federal mental health grants in 1948 it was possible to establish training programs for psychiatrists and mental hospitals began to expand their work in this field. The $500,000 each year that was available was being used mainly to support a large number of small projects. The government grants and the project system were not without difficulties in administration, including delays which made advance planning difficult. The committee recommended that the CMHA establish a flexible scheme for stimulating research in important areas of the mental health field and for the development of top-flight research personnel.

The ad hoc committee was reconvened and in two meetings held in December 1957 and January 1958 prepared further recommendations which were approved by the National Board. The committee advised the Board to establish a fund at the rate of at least $50,000 per annum which would be protected for the use of the research program alone. As soon as possible an endowment should be established which would stabilize the fund.[1]

It was not possible to collect the full $50,000 each year, but amounts in the neighbourhood of half of this were made available. In 1965 a report on the progress made on this project was published.[2] It described the unusual organization of this fund and listed the scientists who received awards, usually $25,000 apiece.

> The fund is, in many ways, unique in its provisions. First it guarantees a stable financing, over three to five years, of a selected worker: he is thus encouraged to establish himself in a research career. Secondly, over the period of award, the researcher is not fettered by administrative details and the requirements of periodic reporting: he is ensured a research climate and a liberal freedom to explore his own ideological themes. And lastly the yearly selection of a lively promising candidate is in the hands of an annually-appointed Director, noted for his broad interests and research sagacity: the selection is on a national basis without restriction as to professional origins.
>
> The National Board of Directors acting as trustees for the Fund, each year, appointed such a suitable person to be the Director of the Fund. Each succeeding Director selected from a large number of applicants one person who in his opinion most merited the support provided by the Research Award.
>
> The Directors of the Fund were: 1959 - Dr. Harvey Cruickshank, Vice President, Bell Telephone Company of Canada Ltd.; 1960 - Dr. Omond Solandt, Chancellor of the University of Toronto, Vice President of The de Havilland Aircraft of Canada Ltd.; 1961 - Dr. Rae Farquharson, Professor Emeritus of Medicine, University of Toronto, Chairman of the Medical Research Council; 1962 - Professor F.C. MacIntosh, Department of Physiology, McGill University, Montreal; 1963 - Dr. Jean Pierre

Cordeau, Vice Dean of Medicine, University of Montreal; 1964 - Dr. John McCreary, Dean of Medicine, University of British Columbia; 1965 - Dr. Chester Stewart, Dean of Medicine, University of Dalhousie; 1966-68 Dr. Robert A. Cleghorn, Professor of Psychiatry, McGill University, Montreal; 1969 - Research Fund discontinued.

Awards from the fund were made to the following:

1959 - The Rev. Dr. Noel Mailloux, Research Centre for Human Relations, Montreal. Projects included the study of attitudes and relationships of boys in reform institutes to family and society.

1960 - Dr. Patrick L. McGeer, Kinsmen Neurological Laboratory, Department of Psychiatry, University of British Columbia. Projects related to the biochemistry of normal and abnormal neural pathways in the brain.

1961 - Dr. Colin M. Smith, Department of Psychiatry, University of Saskatchewan. Projects related to community and home care of psychiatric patients and role of the family physician.

1962 - Dr. John S. Werry, Montreal Children's Hospital. Projects related to psychopharmacology of children.

1963 - Dr. Alex Richman, Department of Psychiatry, University of British Columbia. Projects involved studies on sociology and epidemiology of psychiatric illness.

1964 - Dr. Robert Pos, Department of Psychiatry, University of Toronto. Projects related to the psychiatric implications of sensory deprivation.

1965 - Dr. André Barbeau, Department of Neurology, University of Montreal. Projects related to the possible relationship between Parkinson's Disease and Schizophrenia, the role of L Dopa.

1966 - Replication studies of Niacin in schizophrenia.

1967 - Dr. Benjamin Doane, Department of Psychiatry, Dalhousie University, Halifax, N.S. Projects related to the development of a psychiatric multi-discipline research centre at Dalhousie University.

1968 - Robert D. Hare, Ph.D., Department of Psychology, University of British Columbia. Studies relating to the behavioural modification of psychopathic behaviour.

It was decided to discontinue the project in 1969 partly because of shortfall in meeting budgetary needs across the country but mainly because by that time other sources of funding were becoming available. Moreover, the major funding sources, such as the Medical Research Council in Ottawa and various provincial sources like the Ontario Mental Health Foundation, were not only funding research into mental health problems but were indicating a lively interest in providing for the training and development of research scientists in this field. The concept of providing block grants to individuals to be used for research as desired by the individual still is very slow in being realized.

Public support for mental health programs has always been difficult to establish. In spite of Dr. Hincks' early successes in fund-raising, the years after the Rockefeller Foundation support ceased were difficult, for both the American and the Canadian National organizations. The Government and the United Appeal urged the association from time to time to mount a public fund-raising campaign on its own. Plans for this were indeed discussed and in 1959 a serious study was made. Negotiations were begun with the G.A. Brakeley Co. Ltd., internationally known and respected consultants in fund-raising operations. It was decided as a first venture to explore the possibility of an endowment fund for the Research Program and in May of 1959 the study was completed.[3] It was not very encouraging. It appeared that either the Brakeley people or the executives they interviewed (or both) completely missed the significance of the idea behind the Mental Health Research fund, the notion of block grants to encourage young scientists to proceed with research careers. The strong recommendation in the report was that the CMHA should base its appeal on a specific research project and that a permanent director should be appointed rather than a temporary director changed each year. The Brakeley study was never implemented because its findings were so out of line with the thinking of the Board and the NSPC. No action was taken. It was not until 1986 when the association finally left the Toronto United Appeal that a national campaign was organized.

In 1966 the annual research award was not made. The principal reason for this decision was the mounting publicity concerning the treatment of schizophrenia with large doses of Nicotinic Acid (Vitamin B3). Most of this publicity emanated from the Saskatchewan Division and its scientific advisor, Dr. Ab Hoffer. The NSPC was uneasy about the seemingly extravagant claims made for the efficacy of this treatment.

It was decided that the issue was so important that the money usually budgeted for the annual research award should in 1967 be devoted to a study or several independent studies replicating Dr. Hoffer's work in order to determine if possible the value of the treatment. With Dr. Hoffer's full concurrence and co-operation, a protocol was designed for a series of collaborative studies carried out simultaneously in Canada and other countries. The study was directed by Dr.

Thomas Ban and Dr. Heinz Lehmann of the Douglas Hospital and McGill University, Montreal.

By 1971 several reports were available and consolidated in a progress report which summarized the work completed at that time and the tentative conclusions reached. This provided fresh evidence that schizophrenia was not a single disease but a syndrome with several different root causes. It was posssible that one type of schizophrenia would respond to Vitamin B3 but the concensus was that the side effects were unacceptable and the advantage negligible.[4]

XV

Action on the World Front 1950-60

1. Continuing Support for the WFMH

Many efforts were made by the staff, the National Board, and the National Scientific Planning Council to promote interest and participation by Canadians in the World Federation of Mental Health. National or regional associations having an interest in mental health were invited to join the Federation as member-associations. Individuals were encouraged to join as personal individual members. The WFMH bulletin, published occasionally by the London office of the Federation, was circulated widely. It shortly became a quarterly called *World Mental Health* and contained articles as well as news items of mental health interest from around the globe.

The impact of the London Congress of 1948 continued to influence and expand the concept of mental health, an effect that pervaded the meetings of the Federation's executive board as well as the Fourth International

Congress held in Mexico in 1951. In Canada this led in turn to the suggestion that something in the nature of an International Research Institute on Man should be established. Dr. Hincks had earlier proposed that such an institute be established in Canada on an inter-university basis. The idea was never implemented. However, a standing committee on International Affairs was established by the CMHA Board with Professor Line as Chairman. It stimulated considerable discussion and debate among staff and board members. While the concept of positive mental health and of man as a world citizen endeavouring through co-operation, communication, and social action to protect world peace and world mental health were intriguing and even challenging ideas, the immediate concern and interest of increasing numbers of CMHA members, their local branches, and provincial divisions continued to be the mentally-ill patient and the mental hospital. The growing interest in volunteer programs and in psychiatric research and the exciting possibilities of biochemical and psycho-pharmacologic developments made the objectives of the World Federation seem like an "aspirational evangel," to use a term suggested by Line. Many doubted the ability of the Association to raise money or enlist a large membership for such objectives.*

---

*While a National Research Institute working toward the concept of a "Mentally Healthy Man in a Mentally Healthy World" seemed to be beyond the capacity and resources of a voluntary health organization, it is interesting that Canada and other advanced Western nations have established agencies which are not far removed from this idea. Mainly due to the interest of The Right Honourable Lester B. Pearson, Canada now has an International Development Agency, CIDA with a budget in 1985-86 of nearly two billion dollars dedicated to elevating the health and independence of mankind in the so-called Third World. Dalhousie University in April 1988 announced the foundation of the Brock Chisholm Centre for International Health with similar goals for total health of mankind.

It was finally agreed that the association must somehow combine all these apparently divergent ideas and, while keeping an ideological objective ahead of us, bend our efforts to the immediate problems of the mentally sick and disabled. In earnest of this, it was decided that the CMHA should investigate the possibility of inviting the World Federation to hold its Fifth International Congress in Toronto in 1954. Accordingly in 1952, two member associations, the Canadian Psychological Association and the Canadian Mental Health Association, with the co-operation of the University of Toronto and several other interested organizations, sent an official invitation which was quickly accepted. A congress organizing committee, chaired by Dr. Hincks, was established with Margery King as secretary and Congress executive officer. Line became Chairman of the Program Committee.

2. The Fifth International Congress on Mental Health, 1954

The organizing committee and various sub-committees began to work immediately. Dr. Sidney E. Smith, President of the University of Toronto, became President of the Congress. With his help the university provided an ideal site for the Congress, the theme of which was Mental Health in Public Affairs. There is no doubt that the enterprise held in August 1954 was one of the most successful of its kind ever organized in Canada. Several accounts of the Congress have been published, including the official proceedings. One of the most illuminating summaries of the Congress was a report by Line published in the *Canadian Medical Association Journal* which appears here:

At the University of Toronto during the August just past, a quite unusual Congress was held. Indeed, as the post-Congress period extends itself sufficiently to permit of a thoughtful evaluation of the experience, it is gratifying and challenging to learn of some of the impressions - which appear likely to be lasting impressions - expressed in the accumulating correspondence of those who participated.

From leaders in United Nations and its specialized agencies, from eminent scientists the world over who are engaged in the study of man, from leading citizens of the various continents, we have received comments, unsolicited by the organizing committee of the Congress.

Among those comments, all of which point towards a positive consensus, of first importance is probably that the participants in program and discussion reflected a deep and sincere humility in facing the mental health problems of today's world. In a culture such as ours, where we sometimes feel that the eagerness of psychiatry and clinical psychology and the social sciences generally often leads to over-exaggeration and over-generalization of man's dilemmas, and especially to over-statement of palliatives, solutions, and positive prescriptions, it is extremely significant that the over-all voice of the Congress reflects modesty, humility and, at the same time, determination.

In the second place, and relatedly, there appears to have been sensed an international, a cross-cultural and cross-disciplinary appreciation of the reality of the Congress theme, "Mental Health in Public Affairs." Too often in the past, and indeed in the present, the mental health movement has presented itself, to scientists and citizens alike, as an aspirational evangel, "full of sound and fury," signifying, if not nothing, perhaps something less than nothing; anxiety-provoking without adequate safeguards for social therapy; fund-raising based on human fears,, without adequate action programs; adolescent publicity with little regard for the inherent modesty of science. To have symbolized the fundamental hope that honest partnership among the nations, among the humanistic disciplines, among the serious moral intents of people, can be addressed effectively to the stimulating problems of human society is, if real, a remarkable achievement.

The third impression, expressed universally in the comments received, is a re-awakened faith not only in the value of science of human behaviour - but also in the dignity of the partnership between the scientist and the layman, the citizen. There appears to have been demonstrated the reality of a common cause - man himself and his destiny; not merely his "welfare" in the protective sense, but man as he can, and needs to, become. In other words, while mental health conferences sometimes have given the impression of being superficially concerned with fringe or spectacular items in human living, the comments suggested a renewed faith in the solidarity - spiritually, philosophically, scientifically, practically, - of the design for living that the mental health movement would like to, and is seriously endeavouring to, explore, by all the means at man's disposal.

Fourthly, and, this statement, lastly, the Congress appears to have succeeded in avoiding the impression that one or other of the extremely aggressive "single solutions" or "ideological professions of faith" was trying to capture the field, or to dominate all others. The tower of Babel that could have resulted from warring claims of Materialism versus Idealism, Psychoanalysis and Behaviourism, Love and Discipline in Child Development, and the like, did not materialize. Scientists and citizens addressed themselves to public affairs, man's problems in a one-world context, without endeavouring to provide a single scientific or ideological battering ram to confound all others.

The Congress was organized around five technical sections meeting simultaneously each morning of the week. The Technical Sections were as follows: (a) Public Health and Mental Health Partnership; (b) The Mental Health of Children and Youth; (c) Mental Health in Governmental Activities; (d) Community Partnership in Mental Health;

(e) Professional Advances in Mental Health.

By bringing together over a hundred eminent scientists, who had an opportunity to interchange wisdom and experience, there was guaranteed for the Congress a somewhat unusual galaxy of talent, representing the many disciplines. In the end the Congress could draw on the experience of over 2,000 delegates, practically all of whom participated either in the formal program or voluntary discussion groups. The delegates represented 55 countries and all continents.

It is too early to say as yet what the action corollaries of the Congress will be. A deeper appreciation of the needs and possibilities for research in this field, of multi-disciplinary and cross-cultural design; and increased realization of the importance of the basic partnership between scientist and citizen, especially the citizen exercising responsible judgment in the affairs of man, a realization that current problems in social living of necessity draw the world closer than ever before; these and others may be directions along which we may perhaps evaluate outcome during the perspective of the next five years.[1]

3. World Mental Health Year 1960

The 1950s ended and the new decade began with an event which indicated the recognition achieved by the mental health movement -- World Mental Health Year sponsored by the United Nations and in particular the World Health Organization. Special events were organized to celebrate this year, planned by the Committee on International Affairs of the National Board of Directors. Professor Line presented a report of the Committee to the National Board of Directors in 1959. Excerpts from his report follow:

Six areas of man's immediate and present-day social concerns have been suggested for appropriate consideration: (1) The facts about mental illness, and the treatment of mental illness, as revealed by current knowledge and projected research - in all cultures. (2) Child Development - conditioned by culture, yet reflecting the urgency of childhood in its full potentiality. (3) The training of all professional groups actively concerned with mental health problems. (4) Mental health problems that seem to arise from migration and resettlement. (5) Mental health implications of rapid industrialization. (6) Mental health aspects of aging.

These areas of focus obviously reflect current concerns, the world over.

In Paris, 1961, at the next International Congress we will have an opportunity to give an account of our stewardship, to a world-wide audience. We are accustomed to justifying ourselves as CMHA to our immediate public, lay and professional. In this local context, our Canadian contributions symbolize our concern, in our own parish, with all six areas suggested by those who have planned thoughtfully World Mental Health Year. For example, in the first area, the concerns about mental illness, we have the Tyhurst Report on Canadian Mental Health Services. We have also the experiments of our various Divisions, in the social rehabilitation of ex-hospital patients -experiments and experience that have been sensitively and insightfully reviewed by George Rohn.* In the second area -Child Development - which was our original intrusion beyond Medicine into mental health via Canadian university studies such as those on pre-school children, school age children and shyness. In the third area - Professional Training - we have pioneered, among other things, the Liaison Officer experience in Teacher Training, workshops on the mental

---

*Rohn reported the results of his survey of White Cross Centres at this meeting.

health training of Public Health Nurses. In the fourth area - Migration and Resettlement we have held in our various Divisions discussion workshops with social agencies who are confronted with problems of how to receive immigrants and help them to understand us, to contribute to us by *their* understanding. In area five -Mental health implications of rapid industrialization - many of the Divisions have been engaged in on-going workshops and like activities. In the sixth area - Aging - we have a few items to the credit of our concern, if not of our achievement. We are doing many things which our local situation suggests, we look at many of our social problems mental health-wise, and act with humanism, sympathy, some degree of urgency.

4. The Provincial Divisions

Some appreciation of the achievements as well as difficulties experienced in the various provincial divisions during the 1950s can be gathered from the following extracts from the report of the General Director to the annual meeting of the National Association, held in Halifax, June of 1958.[2]

> Nova Scotia is celebrating the Fiftieth Anniversary of the founding of a voluntary mental health organization in the Province. The decision to hold the Annual Conference and Meeting in Halifax this year represents a tribute which all of us across the country wish to make to the Nova Scotia Division on this occasion.
>
> This division has expanded its work into new branches and has established volunteer CMHA services in several new situations, including the Halifax City Home. The division has rented substantially more space for its office and program activity and has negotiated successfully with two Community Chests (Halifax and Truro).
>
> New Brunswick Division has had a good year. The program of volunteer work so successfully initiated at the mental hospital in Saint John has now been developed with

the same success in Campbellton. I had the pleasure last fall of meeting representatives of the Provincial Board and the Boards of the Branches for a one-day workshop on the organization and progress of CMHA. I think this was useful and is a device to be recommended for all divisions.

Quebec Division has undergone some important changes during the year. The Executive Director, Paul Gelinas, has carefully reorganized the whole staff and has moved the offices to new and much more suitable quarters. The Christmas Gift program was exceptionally well handled last December, and the second annual fund-raising campaign was completed successfully this spring without having to engage the services of a professional fund-raising firm, thus saving literally thousands of dollars. An important community study has been initiated by the Division in co-operation simultaneously with the Montreal Council of Social Agencies and the Counseil des Oeuvres. The study is to be completed by June next year and is being watched closely by the Provincial Scientific Planning Committee. The problems of community organization in Montreal are such that a study of this kind with the fullest co-operation of both the English and the French welfare bodies is absolutely essential. That the Quebec Division was able to bring it about is a signal accomplishment. We are looking forward now to an extension of the Division activities into other localities in addition to Montreal.

In Ontario there have also been some important changes. In January last Admiral Rollo Mainguy, former Canadian Chief of Naval Staff became Executive Director with Mr. J.D. Parks continuing as his assistant. During this year this Division has been very successful in developing a close working relationship with the provincial network of large mental hospitals. In Toronto alone some fifteen different White Cross volunteer activities are now operating. New branches have been formed and others are in the planning stage. The Penny Round Up scheme has continued to grow and now represents an important source of revenue and effective public education project. Since its inception six years ago more than $50,000 has been received by the office in pennies.

Manitoba Division has had a difficult and strenuous year. Some years ago, in order to present a united mental health front, an organization designed solely for volunteer visiting in the mental hospital (called SHARE) agreed to join forces with CMHA. Subsequently, some of the members of the Division Board representing the former SHARE became dissatisfied. In the end the Winnipeg Welfare Council offered its good offices to assist in conducting a critical survey and study of the Manitoba Division. This offer was accepted and now after several months the study has been completed. During this period support from the Community Chest was curtailed. In all honesty I must state that the final recommendations emerging from this affair were not substantially different from recommendations given from time to time both informally and formally by National Office. And furthermore the Division Board itself was proceeding as quickly as it could to implement these suggestions even before the Welfare Council Study was begun. The state of confusion and uncertainty in the community, however, particularly among the social and business leaders, was such that an objective study of this kind was probably necessary and advantageous.

It is clear that certain concepts of administrative and executive responsibility in CMHA are not always understood (or accepted) by some of the community welfare agencies. The recommendation was frequently made in the study, for example, that the Executive Director, and indeed all senior staff, should have extensive professional qualifications (social work, psychology, etc.). It has now been convincingly demonstrated that as far as CMHA organization is concerned administrative, executive and public relations skills are essential in the Executive Director, while professional qualifications are useful but not necessarily essential.

Once again the generality must be tempered by the fact

that different provinces and different communities may require staff with different backgrounds.

In other respects the Manitoba Division is proceeding well in spite of the interruptions in time and energy which the "self-study" imposed. Public Education, professional and lay leadership training, White Cross Volunteer work and rehabilitation and of course the extension into new branches have all been proceeding well.

Saskatchewan Division - the banner division for so many years -once again has had an excellent year with a financial campaign that raised nearly 9 cents per capita in the province. The Rehabilitation Centres in Regina and Saskatoon have been regarded as pilot projects for similar projects beginning in other provinces. It is probable that the present drive to establish a United Fund in Regina will make it difficult for the Regina Branch to avoid becoming involved. The Division is already a member of the Community Chest in Lloydminster.

In Alberta CMHA has undergone complete reorganization. For some time it has been felt that both Calgary and Edmonton Branches ought to be larger operations employing a full time staff. This has finally been brought about by the simple device of creating Northern and Southern Regional sections of the Alberta Division. Each of these Regions has its own Board, staff and office. The Provincial Division office presently is located in the Northern Region office in Edmonton and co-ordination between the two Regions is maintained by the Divisional Board. A fund-raising campaign in February in both Edmonton and Calgary was successful in raising more than $40,000 and plans are now under way for establishing a Social Rehabilitation Centre for discharged mental patients in both Northern and Southern regions.

B.C. has had an interesting but difficult year. To begin with, as was the case with many United Fund drives, last fall the Vancouver Community Chest failed to make its objective and cut backs by as much as 15% were necessary. Since B.C. Division is dependent to a considerable degree on the Vancouver Chest, this has had serious consequences and the program had had to be somewhat curtailed. A very vigorous effort, however, is being made to strengthen the association through membership drives and other fund-raising efforts in areas outside Vancouver.

A major crisis in B.C. occurred during the year which may have implications for the whole organization. The B.C. Government announced a policy of restricting employment of staff for mental and psychiatric institutions. At the same time salary schedules for mental health personnel have remained fixed at an unsatisfactorily low level. The Division took issue with the government on this short-sighted policy at once. Briefs were submitted and public support was mobilized. A slight modification of the government policy was announced but at the moment the situation is still unsatisfactory. In such circumstances it is always difficult to know exactly how far to go in attacking the government. Obviously when aggressive moves against the government are made by the association we are also, if indirectly, attacking the official mental health services and the professional colleagues who have striven so hard to help us. While we feel that we must take a stand in these matters, exactly how far we can go are matters for careful consideration.

Finally I would like to come back to a word about our National structure. In some ways our growth has been slow and not without its difficulties. These were not altogether unexpected. Typical of these difficulties is the problem of relationships between the various parts of our association and the responsibilities one to the other. Thus I am quite sure that it is not easy for a newly established local branch to understand clearly how it relates to the Provincial Division, and why it must assume, right from the beginning, certain financial obligations to the Provincial and National bodies. We are apt to slip into the somewhat complacent attitude that as members of a local branch our only concern and challenge is the program related to the mental health problems of our own community. Certainly there is a feeling - again quite understandable - that these immediate and purely local concerns constitute a priority of interest and obligation if not the limit of them.

Fortunately we are not a loose federation of completely autonomous organizations, each pursuing the mental health goals of our own place in our own way. Rather we are a national corporation, - one organization with the same purpose and objectives, the same basic charter and by-laws imbued with determination to fight mental illness and build mental health on all fronts - National, Provincial, and Local. Our particular genius will lie in our being able to accomplish this feeling of national unity without losing the all-important feeling and challenge of local determinism and responsibility. This can be done (and we are doing it) through constant effort to think first of the organization as OUR organization, something belonging in a very real way to all of us, and through equally diligent effort to avoid the dangers of the split between the WE and THEY or the OURS and THEIRS in our work.*

---

*This clearly indicates the very problems Dr. Hincks worried about when the development of local and provincial branches was first suggested. They are problems rooted in the organization of our country, problems which national voluntary organizations face and even the government worries about. Certainly they are still present in the CMHA.

XVI

Important Issues in Difficult Times 1960-70

1. The Background

The decade 1960-70 was an eventful one. It was the era of the Vietnam war, the Beatles, the hippies, the time of drugs and unhappy protesting youth. It seemed as though the world was headed in a direction leading to the very opposite of mental health and world peace. By 1960, however, the Canadian Mental Health Association was being recognized nearly everywhere as a vigorous and obviously useful national health agency.

The National staff continued to rely on George Rohn, then serving as Director of Program and Development, and Margery King, Director of Education and Training. Alvin Gamble was replaced by Leonard Crainford as Director of Public Information in 1962. The National Scientific Planning Council membership was now expanded from twenty to twenty-five, one from each of the nine provincial divisions and sixteen appointed at large. In order to avoid stagnation, the term of office of these members was three years, about one-third of the members retiring annually.

During the decade the Association went through an agonizing reappraisal of its organization, administration, and constitution. This had begun in the late 1950s with a staff committee on organization. In 1961, Dr. Franc Joubin of Toronto undertook a careful analysis and appraisal of the Association's objectives and structure. His report resulted in the immediate establishment of a joint Committee on Organization comprising The Honourable J.B. Aird and W.L. Laidlaw, together with senior staff and Dr. Joubin. In 1963, Brian Craig was appointed chairman of the Continuing Committee on Organization with Murray Rankin and Judge Ian Dubianski, and in 1964 Gowan Guest headed a Constitutional Committee charged with making the changes in the constitution and by-laws necessary to bring the organizational changes into effect. Most of the changes concerned the number and method of electing and appointing National Board members, the powers and management of the provincial divisions, the method of chartering these divisions, and when necessary removing the charters: Changes in the by-laws were made in 1967, 1968, 1970 and 1972. The last change was recorded in October, 1979.

The mental health grants, which had done so much to improve psychiatric services throughout the country and to establish training programs and research, were finally abandoned. This move caused considerable concern in the CMHA. To some extent their place was taken by federal contributions toward the cost of hospital insurance in 1957 and the medical care insurance which was introduced in

1967. These costs were shared about equally between the provincial and federal governments. In addition, the federal government increased the annual grant to the CMHA in 1966 by $10,000 to a total of $25,000. The was interpreted as a recognition of the advisory and consultative status of the Association which to some extent replaced the Mental Health Advisory Committee of the Department of Health and Welfare which was discontinued in 1969.

The Centennial year, 1967, offered unusual opportunities to push forward a positive mental health program. The annual meeting that year was held in Montreal, the site of Expo 67. To mark the occasion, representatives of the National Association for Mental Health in the United States attended and brought along their famous replica of the Liberty Bell which was sounded in the popular tradition of "Ring the Bell for Mental Health" at a special ceremony at Expo.

As a Centennial project it was suggested that a serious effort be made to record the historic growth and development of the Canadian Mental Health Association since its inception in 1918, nearly fifty years earlier. A start at collecting archival material was made but work on a documentary history and establishment of an archival library did not begin for another decade.*

The death of the inspiring founder, leader, and consultant Clarence Meredith Hincks in 1964 left a gap which would never quite be filled. In the next few years several memorial projects were initiated. The Ontario Mental Health Foundation, a provincial statutory research

---

*This archival library is now located at Queen Street Mental Health Centre, Toronto. It includes the CMHA collection.

funding organization, founded in 1962, established the Hincks Memorial Lectures to be held at irregular intervals sponsored usually by one of the five Ontario university departments of psychiatry. The first of these, held in 1967 at the University of Ottawa, was on the subject "Primary Prevention in Psychiatry." The featured lecturer was Dr. C.A. Roberts who over the years had been a loyal friend of Dr. Hincks and the mental health movement. In addition, the Canadian Mental Health Association organized a Hincks Memorial Scholarship Fund to facilitate the postgraduate education in psychiatry of selected family physicians. This continued successfully for several years in close collaboration with the Canadian College of Family Practice. A third memorial was the reorganization of the Toronto Mental Health Clinic (originally the Mental Hygiene Consultation Service) which became the C.M. Hincks Treatment Centre.

Other grievous losses also occured in 1964. William Line and William E. Blatz who had contributed so much to the development of the CMHA in its first formative period died in that year.

The year 1968 marked the fiftieth anniversary of the founding of the Association. To celebrate this important milestone a gala dinner was organized by a group of members of the Senate and the House of Commons in Ottawa. It was held in the renovated and beautifully decorated Centennial Room of the West Block of the Parliament Buildings. The principal speaker was the Minister of Health and Welfare, the Hon. John Munro.

As a further recognition of this Golden Jubilee, Mr. Leonard Crainford prepared and published a booklet which he called *Probings*. In this were printed some sixty mini-essays written on invitation by Canadians who were leaders in the fields not usually consulted by mental health professionals. They were "artists, teachers, architects, poets, writers and performers." They were asked to "bring their own insights and concerns on... mental health, which they did with passion and conviction." Contributors included Pierre Berton, Northrop Frye, Pierre Elliott Trudeau and Roy Thomson.

2. The Major Accomplishments

With the successful conclusion and final report of the Study on Psychiatric services (the Tyhurst Report *More for the Mind*), it quickly became obvious that three important areas had not been adequately dealt with. These were: Legislative and legal aspects of Mental Disorder; the Psychiatric and Psychological Problems of Children; and the Public Health and Preventive aspects of Mental Health. These were admittedly extensions of the original frame of reference which focused on the care and treatment of mentally ill patients. However, they followed logically and inevitably.

Unfortunately the third one of these tasks (prevention) was not completed at this time, although a start on the project was made and a successful and expanded program on prevention was organized in the 1980s.

(a) The Committee on Law and Mental Disorder

The NSPC quickly started on the first of these problems. A Committee on legislation and psychiatric care was appointed comprising Dr. C.F. Rhodes Chalke, (chairman), Dr. John Dewan, Dr. F.S. Lawson, Dr. Clyde Marshall, Mr. Barry B. Swadron, Prof. F.K. Turner and Dr. J.D. Griffin. By 1969 many others prominent in this field were either added to the Committee or acted as consultants providing helpful advice and direction. The committee met regularly twice a year and, as the Tyhurst Committee had done, invited consultants from other appropriate disciplines to meet with it. It produced three reports on different aspects of the problem, *Hospitals and Patient Care*, 1964, *Civil Rights and Privileges*, 1967, and *Criminal Process*, 1969.[1] In 1973 a revised and up-dated edition of these three reports, combined in one book, was prepared by Mr. Barry B. Swadron and Mr. Donald R. Sullivan.[2] This edition was dedicated to the late J.S.D. Tory, Q.C., past president of the Association. Mr. Tory had played an important role in promoting the development of the Association during the 1960s and had been particularly interested in the work of this committee.

(b) Study on Canadian Children

As early as 1962 there was considerable concern being expressed by the National Board as well as the NSPC about the obvious lack of appropriate facilities for the treatment and education of children with emotional and learning problems. By this time the Canadian Association for Retarded Children* had established strong national and provincial organizations and was anxious to collaborate in a major study on children with learning disorders. Dr. Malcolm Beck of Prince Edward Island was active in both these national associations and several liaison meetings were held. Eventually in 1964 a consortium of national associations all vitally concerned with the mental health of

---

*This association changed its name to the Canadian Association for the Mentally Retarded (CAMR) and currently is called the Canadian Association for Community Living (CACL).

children came together to form the Commission on Emotional and Learning Disorders in Children, (CELDIC). Before the study was well under way, seven organizations were involved: The Canadian Mental Health Association, The Canadian Association for the Mentally Retarded, The Canadian Education Association, The Canadian Council on Children and Youth, The Canadian Rehabilitation Council for the Disabled, The Canadian Welfare Council, and the Dr. Barnardo's organization. Financial support for the study came from several sources, including the federal government and Dr. Barnardo's. An executive committee chaired by a very dedicated businessman, Mr. R.H. Shannon, was assembled and a task force with two co-chairmen, Dr. Denis Lazure and Dr. C.A. Roberts, both of Montreal. The executive secretary of the project was Dr. Margery King. There followed many months of hard work, field trips, surveys, special reports, and studies. The final report was assembled and published by the CMHA in 1970 under the arresting title of *One Million Children*.

"We are convinced", the report stated, "that two things are required: much greater integration of the efforts of government, not just at different levels but especially between departments and services; and far more responsibility for decisions that affect the life of a child to be taken by those who are close to the child.

With the best intentions in the world, it is impossible for someone sitting in Ottawa or in a provincial capital miles away to decide what is best for any individual child; the state makes a poor parent. The decisions that affect how we will meet the child's need can be taken only in his local community where he can be viewed as a human being. He must be seen as a whole child in the context of his life situation, not as a problem, not as a case, a file or a number, but as a child who needs our help. To provide continuity of care and immediate help when it is required, decisions about what is needed must be made by people close to the child in his home, school and community. We are firmly convinced that this is essential if we are to be able to help children with emotional and learning disorders.

In the Committee we talked a great deal about the people who care. We are all agreed that *people* are at the core of any helping process. The best organizational system can fail if the people implementing it are inept. But if the people really care, they can be helpful despite an inadequate plan or with poor equipment."[3]

Many believe this study was the most important document concerning troubled children ever produced in Canada. One of the supporting studies on Children in Residential Care was prepared by Professor Quentin Rae-Grant and Patricia Moffat. Because of its special importance, it was published by the CMHA.[4]

A third related project was a conference planned by the Quebec Division in co-operation with the National Office and the World Federation for Mental Hygiene. It was held in 1969 and dealt with the Legal Rights of Children. The principal papers were published by the Rotary Club of Montreal.

These three publications relating to children were all produced through collaboration of the CMHA with other organizations. They represent an important achievement in delineating not only problems faced by so many Canadian children but the appropriate solutions as well.

3. Mental Health Aspects of Public Health

In 1968 the NSPC recommended that the National Board establish a committee or task force to study the preventive programs in the field of mental health which could be built in to local and provincial public health programs. Several small committee meetings were held in 1968 and 1969, and in May 1969 an ad hoc group assembled to tackle this project under the chairmanship of Dr. John B. Macdonald, former president of the University of British Columbia. The study began with a detailed review of the literature with special attention to three factors: The role of social factors causing irrrational behaviour; the factors basic to the maintenance of good mental health; and public health considerations in the treatment of mental disease. The study was initiated with the assistance of a modest federal government grant. The provincial Deputy Minister of Health, Welfare and Education and other key persons were contacted requesting information concerning actual or potential programs now going on in these areas and ideas for new programs. Miss Patricia Moffat, who had been active in the CELDIC Study Committee, was appointed Project Director.

During 1970 the work planned was carried out. Guidelines for policies and programs were drafted. However later in the year the Ministry of Health and Welfare changed the focus of its research support in order to develop demonstration projects related to the cost and patterns of the delivery of health services. An attempt was made to fit the Canadian Mental Health Association project into these new guidelines, but the Department could not see the role of a voluntary organization carrying out studies of this kind. Support therefore discontinued.

After careful consideration the NSPC decided to recommend that the project on Public Health and Preventive Aspects of Mental Health be tabled at least temporarily and that major effort be made to help the provincial divisions and the local branches develop programs related to the implementation of the recommendations of the CELDIC Report. Miss Moffat's time was rescheduled to allow her to assist in this endeavor. During the next few months she visited all the provincial divisions and helped promote support and understanding of the issues and proposals presented in the report.

Although the Public Health and Preventive Aspects of Mental Health Project was quietly dropped, the problem of prevention was an-ever present challenge and was again attacked with great vigour in 1982 with the preparation and publication of a major report on the theory and practice of preventive action (Chapter XIX).

XVII

Social and Political Action 1960-75

1. Presentation of Briefs

During this decade the Association became very busy preparing briefs and reports which were presented formally to government departments, Royal Commissions, Commissions of Inquiry, and Select Committees at the federal and provincial levels.[1]

These briefs were usually drafted by committees of the NSPC with National Board participation. Others represented collaborative presentations prepared with other voluntary or professional associations. Reference has previously been made of the brief presented by Committees of the NSPC to the Select Committee of the House of Commons in 1953, to the Royal Commision on Insanity as a Defence in Criminal Cases in 1954, and to the Department of Citizenship and Immigration on several occasions. Other examples were the following:

222

(a) *Submission to the Cabinet 1960*

A brief was presented by the President (Mr. J.S.D. Tory) and a small delegation of the National Board members and senior staff to the Prime Minister, The Right Honourable John Diefenbaker and members of his cabinet in 1960. This occasion was utilized to emphasize a number of principles which the Association believed should guide government policy and action. With reference to *immigration* the following points were made; the need to correct various misconceptions such as the idea that once a person is judged mentally ill (or "insane" in legal terminology) he will always be mentally ill; the acceptance of the idea that immigrants who become insane can often be treated successfully with a good prognosis; the recognition of the fact that holding a deportation order over the head of such an immigrant might well mitigate against the successful treatment and, finally, the need to revise and modernize the terminology used with refernce to mental illness, i.e., "idiot, moron," etc. On *mental health research*, the need for the provision of adequate funds for modern scientific research on the causes, treatment, and prevention of mental illness, was stressed. On *hospital insurance* the inclusion of mental and psychiatric hospitals under the insurance act was urged.

(b) *Royal Commision on Health Services, 1962*

This submission to the Hall Commision was presented in May 1962. It was based largely on the findings of the Committee on Psychiatric Services (the Tyhurst Committee) but included, in addition, sections on legislation, mentally disordered children, the economics of mental illness, and a concluding section on prevention. The

Dr. John Clayton, professional and scientific director (1972-1977).
Source: CMHA Collection, QSMHC Archives

Gordon Morwood, Director of Planning and Development since 1975.
Source: CMHA Collection, QSMHC Archives

Dr. Robert Martin, Chairman of the National Scientific and
Planning Council (1979-1983) and National President (1984-1986).

Source: CMHA Collection, QSMHC Archives

Mr. E. Austin Fricker, National President of CMHA (1987 -).

Source: CMHA Collection, QSMHC Archives

presentation was made by the President, Judge Ian V. Dubienski, Q.C., of Winnipeg, Dr. Tyhurst, and Dr. Griffin. It was one of the most comprehensive briefs ever made by the Association to a federal Royal Commission.

After the Commission Report appeared, the CMHA prepared a further statement about it. The Board of Directors and the NSPC strongly endorsed most of the recommendations relating to mental health, and noted that of the 256 recommendations the 29 which were relevant to mental health and mental illness were placed first. It was felt that the emphasis thus given to mental health would help to develop and strengthen Canadian public opinion in favour of the kind of reforms long advocated by the Association. It will be recalled that the keynote recommendation of the report, *More for the Mind* emphasized the proposition that "Mental illness should be dealt with in the same organizational, administrative and professional framework as physical illness and that patients suffering from mental illness should receive the same excellence of medical and ancillary health services as quickly, as easily, and as efficiently as do the patients suffering from physical illness." (Chapter XIII).

Recommendation 29 of the Commission's Report stated this principle even more eloquently. It urged:

> "That henceforth all the discrimination in the distinction between physical and mental illness in the organization and provision of services for the treatment and the attitudes upon which these discriminations are based be disavowed for all time as unworthy and unscientific."

(c) Divorce 1966

In December 1966, a submission was presented to the Special Joint Committee of the Senate and House of

Commons on Divorce. In this presentation the Association was represented by the National President, Gowan T. Guest, and the General Director. The submission addressed the following principles: mental and emotional disorders frequently underlie marriage breakdown and are also important in understanding the distress and behavioural difficulties of the children of such families; "chronic unsoundness of mind" should definitely not be a legal reason for allowing divorce because such people often recover completely; conciliation procedures, family therapy, and marriage counselling need strengthening and solid support; there is no guarantee that such measures will prevent complete breakdown but their full and expert application has not been tried.

(d) Immigration 1967

The following year (1967), a joint submission by the Canadian Mental Health Association and the Canadian Association for Retarded Children (now the Association for Community Living) was made to the Special Joint Committee of the Senate and House of Commons on Immigration. This brief again stressed the problems posed by use of obsolete psychiatric terms in current legislation relating to persons denied admission to Canada. In addition it urged that a person suffering from a verified mental disorder who is a member of a family otherwise admissible, should not be prohibited admission where the potential positive contribution of the whole family is significant; that where there is doubt about the eligibility of an immigrant on the basis of his mental condition, a tribunal of professionals representing appropriate disciplines should assist the Department in reaching a decision; and that a more careful preparation and orientation of immigrants for life in Canada be organized to help prevent breakdown due to impact of sudden environmental change and so-called "culture shock."

(e) Second Submission to Cabinet 1967

In the same year (1967), another submission was formally presented to the Prime Minister, The Right Honourable Lester B. Pearson, and his cabinet in Ottawa. The presentation was made by the President of the CMHA, Mr. Gowan T. Guest, and other senior members of the Board of Directors. Because of its range of topics and the increasing sense of urgency expressed, the recommendations are presented here in some detail:

(1) The Hospital Insurance and Diagnostic Services Act, 1957 should be amended so that all mental and psychiatric hospitals are covered under the act.

(2) Training grants should be individually increased in amounts and greatly extended.

(3) The federal government should collaborate with national voluntary and professional organizations in establishing pilot projects and surveys and in providing in-service training programs for non-psychiatric professionals such as general practitioners, public health nurses, teachers and the clergy.

(4) Programs of research into the cause, treatment and control of mental illness should be greatly expanded, co-ordinated and accelerated.

(5) The mental health division of the Department of National Health and Welfare should be strengthened and reorganized to ensure that the highest quality of professional advice is available not only to the department

itself, but also to other departments of government where issues relating to psychiatric and mental problems arise, and that effective leadership in mental health planning and program is available to the provincial governments.

(6) The federal government should support programs to study the mental health services for children in order to provide guidelines for the development of integrated services and facilities for the early detection, treatment and prevention of such disorders.

(7) The federal government should not only guarantee that the National Medical Services Insurance Program includes psychiatric treatment but also institute studies immediately to resolve the potential duplication and overlap, between treatment provided on a private (insured) basis and treatment provided by provincial governmental mental hospitals and clinics.

(8) A National Psychiatric Advisory Board or Council should be appointed and a suitable working relationship established with the psychiatric and behavioural science departments of appropriate universities.

(9) Consultation, guidelines and financial incentives should be provided to increase the number and effectiveness of industrial rehabilitation workshops for patients recovering from mental illness.

(10) The Immigration Act and its regulations should be amended and that every effort be made in this amendment to take into account sound medico-social concepts and principles.

(f) Science Policy 1969

In 1969 a brief prepared in collaboration with the CPA addressed to the Senate Special Committee on Science Policy again stressed the need for establishing adequate budgets and security for scientific research in mental health. It was pointed out that there was a particular need for clinical research by medical and psychiatric practitioners who would require training and motivation to enter this field. The value of block grants in addition to project grants and the stipulation that a certain proportion of the general health research budget be utilized in this way were also emphasized. The CMHA's collaborative Nicotinic Acid study, where similar projects were run simultaneously in various sometimes widely, separated centres, was describesd as a desirable procedure in some problem areas.

(g) Justice and Legal Affairs 1967

Another joint submission by the CAMR (now the CACL) and the CMHA was presented in 1967 to the House of Commons Committee on Justice and Legal Affairs. This brief dealt mainly with several points at issue, such as the need for a uniform age across Canada under which a person must be dealt with in a Child and Family Court, the use and abuse of indeterminate sentences (they should be regularly reviewed and in any case never allowed to run more that ten years), and the need for a judge to hear certain evidence concerning criminal cases before ordering a medical examination to determine fitness to stand trial by reason of insanity. Otherwise it wàs contended that there was a risk of committing a person to a mental institution on a Lieutenant-Governor's Warrant for an indeterminate time when in fact the person may not have committed the alleged offence in the first place.

(h) Non-Medical Use of Drugs 1974

In the same year a brief was presented to the Commission

of Inquiry into the Non-Medical Use of Drugs. The Association went on record opposing jail sentences for young people convicted of "simple possession" of cannabis. It was strongly in favour of a strengthened education and research program and made specific suggestions concerning improving treatment and rehabilitation in which community resources would be utilized much more fully.

(i) Suicide 1974

During this same year a careful study was completed on the growing rate of suicide and suicidal attempts in Canada. A brief was presented to the Minister of Justice urging that attempted suicide be removed as an indictable offence from the Criminal Code.

In looking back over this period it should give a sense of satisfaction to those involved in the Association to realize that by 1975 most of the recommendations advanced in these briefs had been implemented.

2. National Conferences

In addition to the preparation and presentation of briefs and submissions, the social and political action program of the Association during the 1960s included the organization of several national conferences. Some of these also were collaborative efforts with other national voluntary and professional associations. Included were the following:

(a) Student Mental Health 1963

This dealt with the extent of emotional, social, and psychiatric problems in college students and the treatment service available to them. It was co-sponsored by the

CMHA, the National Federation of Canadian University Students, and the World University Student Service, and held in May, 1963 at Queen's University, Kingston, Ontario. Some two hundred delegates attended.

(b) Medical Action for Mental health 1964

This was co-sponsored by the Canadian Medical Association and the CMHA. It was held in March 1964 at the Chateau Laurier Hotel, Ottawa. The Conference was based on the report *More for the Mind* and was geared to promote understanding and implementation of its chief recommendations. About three hundred psysicians attended. The conference was addressed by the Prime Minister, The Right Honourable Lester B. Pearson, and other representatives of the federal government.

(c) The William Line Seminar (on Mental Health in Education) 1968

This mini-conference brought together most of his former colleagues and students including the teachers who had been part of the liaison officer course originally initiated by the CMHA. It was held in March 1968 as a memorial to this great man. The theme was "The Person in the Process."

(d) Seminar for Overseas Students 1969

This was sponsored jointly by the CMHA, the World Federation for Mental Health, and the Canadian International Developement Agency. It was designed for students from developing countries who were studying in Canada in any of the mental health disciplines. About thirty five students attended the three-day seminar in November 1969. Because of the obvious reluctance of some of these students to return to the country of their origin, it was strongly recommended that students should receive basic training in the mental health professions in their own countries. A year or more spent in Canada after such training would be advantageous. It would also be useful for Canadian consultants and the teachers to be assigned for a tour of duty in these countries.

XVIII

Approaching the Eighties

By the end of the 1960s, the reorganization of the Association had been completed and a program of social and political action fully implemented. Public and professional education on mental health through very well-conceived programs and conferences was underway. Local community and provincial programs were developing healthy autonomy which encouraged an attack on local and regional problems. Nevertheless, some of the old problems persisted. Reports of inadequate and even discriminatory treatment of patients in mental and psychiatric hospitals were receiving publicity. There was a feeling that some of the mental hospitals were not practising a sufficiently high standard of medical and psychiatric care. The criticism and antagonism directed to the psychiatric specialty was growing; the old bogey of insufficient and insecure financial support for the CMHA was, if anything, becoming more prominent.

1. Accreditation of Mental Hospitals

Since the early days of the Canadian National Committee, Dr. Hincks had been concerned about the need for some standardized method of evaluating mental hospitals. The National Committee in the U.S had already established a pattern for surveying mental hospitals and mental health sevices in various states. By the early 1920s the Medical Director, Dr. Thomas W. Salmon, and his assistant, Dr. Frankwood Williams, were devoting almost full time to this project. Dr. Hincks and Dr. Clarke were most interested in their work, and the first major projects of the Canadian National Committee were of this kind. Occasionally, in later years, the Mental Hospital Division of the American National Committee was utilized in helping with surveys of the larger provinces like Ontario and Quebec.

The American College of Surgeons for years had been accrediting general hospitals in both the United States and Canada. By the 1930s some of the Canadian mental hospitals were also being accredited by this body. After the war the interest in accreditation increased, and it was felt that the rather superficial examination by the American College was really not as helpful as it might be. A Joint Commission on Accreditation of Hospitals was formed in 1952, comprising the American College of Surgeons, the American Hospital Association, and the American College of Physicians. Canadian representation on this commission was invited and accreditation of Canadian general hospitals became more meaningful. Evaluation of the Canadian Mental Hospitals was still inadequate.

The American Psychiatric Association also had a long-standing interest in establishing standards for mental hospitals and services. Publication of APA standards appeared after World War II and was frequently revised and updated. The survey conducted by the American Psychiatric Association of the British Columbia mental health service in 1959-60 aroused some criticism and hostility among Canadian psychiatrists because it seemed to ignore completely not only the CMHA but the Canadian Psychiatric Association which by this time had become very vigorous. The fact that the APA report was aggressively negative about the services reviewed did not help. The standards set up by the APA seemed unrealistic and out of line with Canadian experience.

In the meantime, a Canadian Council on Hospital Accreditation had been formed with a Board of Directors representing the Canadian Medical Association, the Canadian Hospital Association, the Royal College of Physicians and Surgeons, and l'Association de Medicin de Langue Francais. One of the members nominated by the CMA was Dr. Burdett McNeel, a former chairman of the NSPC and a member of the Tyhurst Committee. He held this membership in the Accreditation Council from 1958 to 1967 and was deeply invoved in persuading the Council to extend their survey activities to include mental hospitals. The CMHA procured a grant of $2,000 to assist the Council in conducting trial runs on selected institutions.

Between 1962 and 1964, trial surveys were completed by Dr. William Taylor, the executive director of the Council and Dr. Burdett McNeel, in several provincial mental hospitals (Selkirk, Man.; Dartmouth, N.S.; Verdun, P.Q.; and New Toronto,Ont.). As a result, an accreditation guidebook for mental hospitals was developed and finally published in 1967. This guidebook was used for several years and has undergone extensive revision. Accreditation now deals not only with mental hospitals but with all types of mental health centres including psychiatric units of general hospitals and mental health clinics.

2. Financial Support and the United Way

The Association established a co-operative working relation with the Toronto Community Chest (United Way) when the latter was first organized in the 1930s. The original contract provided a grant from the Chest equal to the amount of money which had been collected annually in Toronto by the National Committee. An additional grant was made during the war to defray the cost of establishing the Mental Hygiene Consultation Service, but when this service became an independent Toronto Mental Health Clinic, the extra grant was discontinued. In the meantime, the National Committee was growing rapidly and the Ontario Division and Metro Toronto Branch began operations and the Community Chest was concerned over the greatly increased demands for support. The development of three parts of the organization requiring support instead of one was very disturbing, especially since a number of other national health agencies with local branches were beginning to appear. The threat of multiple campaigns for the "charity dollar" had to be avoided if possible.

During this time the United Way type of fund-raising had spread across the country, and one after another of the provincial divisions and local branches were seeking admission or were being pressured to enter such schemes. But, apart from Toronto, with its long experience with the National Committee, these new Community Funds had little interest or feeling of responsibility for providing a "fair share" of the support for the National Office.

In the next few years a new develpment emerged, the

National Agency Review Committee (NARC). This was an attempt through the Canadian Welfare Council in Ottawa to prevent a complete breakdown in relations between the national voluntary organizations and the local federated funds. The idea was that each national organization would appear before a neutral panel of informed laymen to present their program and budgetary needs. The panel would prepare an independent report which would be widely circulated to all Chests and Funds, giving its appraisal of the program and budget with its recommendations, positive or negative.

This development was followed generally by similar agency review committees established locally for provincial and local branches of national agencies. While this worked well in theory, in practice it seemed, to the national agencies at least, that very little attention was paid by the Community Funds to the NARC reports. The attitude always seemed to be "let's keep the money raised in local federated funds for local agency programs." Added to this was a growing feeling that Community Chests should not have to fund the national association for the "horrible diseases." The Cancer, Heart, and Tuberculosis (later Respiratory Diseases) Associations never agreed to join in the first place. Others who joined and then opted out of the federation funding found it difficult to re-establish a fund-raising campaign on their own. In 1972 the NARC was discontinued and in 1986 the CMHA - United Way partnership was dissolved.

3. The Forces of Reaction

The reaction growing against the mental health movement, however, was much broader than criticisms coming from the Community Chests. The Annual report of the General

Director for 1958 stated:

There is another national problem which I want to refer to in passing, which is going to cause some anxiety. This is the wave of reaction which is sweeping across the country and which all too readily attracts to its bandwagon an increasing number of citizens. This has emerged for example as an aggressive attack against the so-called "frills" in our academic education program. With the re-emphasis on the importance of the 3 Rs and the implied threat of the Russian Sputnik, we are warned to stop mollycoddling our youngsters, to throw out time-wasting procedures such as mental health courses and guidance counselling and to develop a real "get tough" attitude at home and in school. I have noticed that concern with this "get tough" attitude is reflected also among some professional people in their discussion of welfare and health programs. Thus, a speaker at the annual meeting of the Montreal Council of Social Agencies stated that in her opinion there had been far too much talk about mental health and mental illness and it was time we did something really important like attacking the housing and the unemployment situation instead. Somewhat the same attitude was reflected in a recent Toronto conference on Public Relations for Social Agencies, where an informal poll seemed to indicate that many believed that Mental Health was getting far too much attention. It has happened before. I think we must be prepared, however to cope immediately and vigorously with misinformation and misleading implications. This is a challenge for stepping up our program of public education, not retreating from it.[1]

4. The State of the Nation's Mental Health.

The range and depth of CMHA activities across the country at the end of the 1960s may be appreciated by these excerpts from the Report of the General Director, Annual Meeting, June, 1969. While some of the activities may seem somewhat out of date by current practices, they do represent an important phase in the history and development of mental health policies.

At the Federal Government level undoubtedly the most significant mental health action during the last twelve months has been the amendments to the Criminal Code. These removed homosexual acts "between consenting adults" from the Code and gave some legality to the growing practice in Canada of therapeutic abortions.

Another part of the new act, however, was of even more mental health importance. It refered to the problem of "unfitness to stand trial." Under the new act evidence could be heard sufficient to determine whether there was a strong likelihood of guilt before the issue of unfitness was determined. In suitable cases where there was actually little or no evidence of guilt, it was then possible to acquit the person instead of sending him for an indeterminate period in a custodial mental hospital. This amendment was suggested in presentations made by the CMHA to the Parliamentary Committee on the Criminal Code in 1967, and was also one of the recommendations contained in Part 3 of the report *The Law and Mental Disorder* published by CMHA early in 1969. The amendment to the Code further makes it mandatory to review patients confined in mental hospitals under such conditions at regular intervals (another recommendation from CMHA).

The Medical Research Council in Ottawa has recently announced an enlarged program of research and fellowship grants. Many of the basic research projects funded through this Council have pertinence for the mental health field. More important is the fact that the MRC has established more than 300 research fellowships which have tenure of up to three or four years. Some of these have gone to scientists working in the mental health field. This is a policy adopted by the CMHA long ago, demonstrated in a very modest way through the policies of our national Mental Health Research Fund and frequently recommended to governments and foundations.

The Federal Hospital Insurance plan introduced in the late 1950s still excluded mental hospitals. In spite of this lack of recognition by the Federal Government in sharing the cost of this type of care, several of the provinces have put such hospitals under the wing of the Provincial Hospital Insurance Commissions so that they are covered unilaterally so to speak. The CMHA still insists that this lack of Federal Government action is unfair both to psychiatric hospitals and to the provinces.

Time does not permit a lengthy report of new developments in all provinces but a few highlights may be in order. One of the most importrant of these has been the publication of the report on the Alberta Mental Health Study (The Blair Report). This fine survey and report is one of the most revealing, as well as complete studies in depth of the mental health services to be carried out in this country. The Alberta Government is to be congratulated on its unswerving support of this study even though its findings have been drastically critical of government services. Many of the principles and recommendations followed closely those of the Tyhurst Report, *More for the Mind*.

In New Brunswick a report on the mental health services by a Special Citizens' Committee appointed by the government and co-chaired by Mr. Travis Cushing, Vice-President of this Association, has been completed, submitted, and now is under careful study in connection with implementation.

In Prince Edward Island a new mental health act has replaced obsolete and antiquated legislation. This act like the one in Ontario follows very closely the principles contained in Part I of the report of the CMHA, *The Law and Mental Disorder*.

Nova Scotia, has gone further than most provinces in implementing the principles of *More for the Mind*, and is bringing its health legislation up to date. The government is also proposing to expand the services of the community mental health clinics to include programs of prevention and public education - activities formerly carried out by CMHA.

In Saskatchewan a program of decentralizing mental health services has progressed to the point where the two large mental hospitals have reduced their patient population significantly. This means that the government, in collaboration with voluntary organizations, including CMHA, must very rapidly develop an effective program of rehabilitation and aftercare. This program is being watched with great interest by experts all over North America.

In Ontario the program introduced by the Minister of Health, Dr. M. Dymond, and his associates, whereby the outpatients and community mental health services are developed principally in appropriate general hospitals as part of the general hospital psychiatric services, has continued to grow. General hospitals, traditionally rather wary of becoming involved too deeply in community programs, are now recognizing that, in mental health services at any rate, they must indeed integrate their work with the voluntary and other agencies of the community. An excellent example of this is in the program established by two general hospitals in Scarborough (Scarborough General and the Centennial General) in the east end of Metropolitan Toronto.

In Quebec the outstanding accomplishment during the last year was the successful organization of a conference unique in the history of mental health programs. This conference brought more than 500 people together so that the younger generation were able to meet, in face-to-face confrontation and dialogue the older generation (the establishment) on such issues as education, industry, religion, health and welfare, and so on. The Quebec Division is also proceeding towards a reorganization of its structure so that its branches will coincide appropriately with the provincial regional mental health programs already referred to above.

Work at the national level of our Association has been principally concentrated in three areas, reflecting the responsibilities of the three senior staff members in the office. Mr. Leonard Crainford has been responsible for developing a national program of public information . . . Mr. George Rohn has been responsible for consultation and guidance in the administration and financial field, while Griffin has assumed the responsibility for the scientific and technical program with the guidance of our very able National Scientific Planning Council.

It has been decided to explore the possibility of studying the usefulness of volunteers in elementary schools working with emotionally-disturbed children, as a preventive program. A Committee is at work charged with producing guidelines for the selection, orientation and supervision of this kind of activity.

In spite of all this worthwhile activity, there is within the organization a very healthy spirit of dissatisfaction with those programs which are becoming increasingly expensive, time-consuming, and difficult or impossible to evaluate. At the same time there is an understandable reluctance to depart from the old just for the sake of change for something new. The problem needs objective examination and study. In the end the hard work and even anxiety and tension created will pay off in the development of a much more realistic and effective program and a more efficient association.[2]

XIX

Postscript to a New Era

1. A New General Director and a New Symbol

The 1970s ushered in another new era with new problems. Dr. Griffin retired and was replaced by Mr. George Rohn. The White Cross as a symbol was replaced by a new and very original symbol or logo which is now nationally used by the association.

Mr. Leonard Crainford, who had been Director of Information Services for several years, developed this new symbol, the origin of which he always delighted to explain thus:

(a) Four arrows indicate the four principle directions of the association's concern: (1) service to patients; (2) survey and social action; (3) public education; and (4) scientific research.

(b) The arrows became larger, indicating growth of concern, but there is still nothing to indicate local or national *action*.

(c) The arrows became indentical triangles to indicate areas of increasingly effective action.

(d) The triangles became more irregular in shape, indicating flexibility, but together make a strong cohesive square representing united effort.

(e) A visual focal point, a circular dot, provides a dynamic and intriguing creation - a healthy vibrant figure standing for a cryptic form of the official name - Mental Health Canada. This form was quickly adopted as the informal designation for the various divisions and branches of the association, so there is Mental Health, Ontario, Mental Health, Halifax and so on.

With the retirement of Dr. Griffin in 1971, the organization for the first time in its history was left without a medical person and psychiatrist on its senior executive staff. Mr. Rohn, who succeeded Griffin as General Director, was a qualified psychiatrist social worker and thoroughly competent organizer and administrator. There was some uneasiness among the National Board members about the lack of a medical staff person at National headquarters. This was relieved when Dr. John Clayton, a psychiatrist recently retired from the Ontario Mental Health Service, joined the staff as Director of Professional Development. When he in turn resigned in 1977, there was no psychiatric replacement available and the post was filled by professionals from non-psychiatric disciplines. There was some speculation among psychiatrists that this represented a drifting away by the CMHA from organized psychiatry and a rejection of the medical model of mental illness. However, in January 1978, Dr. Clayton, in a letter to the author, stated:

> From my point of view, my years with the Canadian Mental Health Association were both my most productive and happiest. I have a very fat file containing copies of scores of documents; reports, position papers, and submissions to various Government Committees or commissions, prepared and presented during those years. They reflected the co-operation, thinking and (often hours of) deliberation of scores of professional and lay volunteers (mostly from or within the National Scientific and Planning Council).
>
> Many of these documents are still current (some still "before their time"). Some are still in use. Sadly there are many other recommendations and concepts born in NSPC committees and in the CMHA during those years which perhaps, like seeds, are dormant and buried. If they are like seeds, than a new prosperity may, like spring, awaken them

in other minds and in times when new action and reform can occur.[1]

2. Concern About the Medical Model

When Dr. Hincks first began to plan the professional and scientific work of the Association, he used to bemoan the fact that the very last professional group to take an interest in mental hygiene would be the medical profession. In those days, indeed, there were very few adequately trained psychiatrists and none very interested in basic research. The interested professionals who were readily available were people like E.A. Bott, W.E. Blatz, W. Line, D. Ketchum, and S. Laycock, all psychologists. Blatz had his MD. but seldom emphasized his medical role. There were some psychiatrists in Montreal, like Mundie, Mitchell, and Silverman, but they were not as deeply involved in the organization or as close personally to Hincks as the Toronto group. It was not until D. Ewen Cameron headed the department at McGill that a solid partnership with psychiatric departments in the universities developed.

Cameron and Griffin were both involved in the early formative period of the Canadian Psychiatric Association, and it was Griffin's objective to build a very strong liason with this branch of medicine. Fortunately, as an officer of the Canadian Psychiatric Association, he had a foot in each camp. This strong liason was reflected also in the increasingly dominant role played by psychiatrists on the NSPC and its various committees. The important Tyhurst Committee was made up entirely of psychiatrists. It was originally conceived as the Committee on Mental Health Services, but later was called the Committee on Psychiatric Services. Even the prestigious multi-agency sponsored Commission on Children (CELDIC) was co-chaired by two psychiatrists.

By the 1970s some of the local CMHA branches and divisions were beginning to respond sympathetically to current anti-medical and anti-psychiatric sentiments commonly expressed by former patients. Stimulated by growing concerns about patients' rights, groups were organizing and becoming very vocal in their protest against involuntary committal to mental hospital, and the increased use of drugs in treatment. The use of surgical procedures such as lobotomy had virtually disappeared by this time but the electro-convulsive therapy still had medical and psychiatric approval in selected cases. This form of treatment became an important bone of contention and the substantial evidence supporting the value of ECT was simply ignored. The emotional image of being "electrocuted" and the rumors of consequent brain damage and permanent memory loss became familiar rallying arguments for the anti-psychiatric and anti-medical groups. Basically, the criticism was directed along two lines: (1) the individual rights and freedoms sponsored by the civil liberties groups were being violated and (2) the power of the medical profession and its claimed skill and knowledge were resented. There were some respected professionals, even psychiatrists, who supported this criticism, and it is not suprising that many lay members of the CMHA became responsive and sympathetic to those who opposed the "medical model" of mental illness. There seemed to be no psychiatrist clearly identified with the CMHA who was able to close the widening breach.

3. Unification and Consolidation

From the begining of the association, there had been a strong interest in prevention of mental illness and the concept of promoting positive mental health. For some, this took on a new importance after the war. Mental illness and mental hospitals were no longer the central concern. The need for a liaison with the physicians who were responsible for these institutions seemed less important. In his annual report for 1969, President J.F. O'Sullivan stated:

> The time is past for primary attention to be given to mental illness. The day has come for priority to be given to mental health, developing research and facilities for prevention, youth unrest, and alienation of the disadvantaged.

In many local branches, however, members were still deeply invoved in activities related to mentally ill patients, such as support and rehabilitation programs for those discharged from mental hospitals. It seemed that some parts of the association were going their own way on a path somewhat different from that agreed to at national annual meetings and conferences. In 1970 a National Program Review Committee was appointed to study this problem and recommend steps to promote co-ordination and unity.

Toward the end of the 1970s three events helped to bring about a more positive development. One was the expansion of the NSPC by Dr. Clayton into a national network of over eighty scientists, many of them representing disciplines such as anthropology, sociology and community organization. Psychiatry, while still important, was now one of several disciplines concerned with planning and organizing truly significant mental health community programs. The second was the initiative taken by George Rohn when, following a rather critical letter by a senior psychiatrist published in the bulletin of the Canadian Psychiatric Association, he wrote the editor proposing a meeting to discuss the issues and try to close the ranks again. Meetings were held and at the time of writing (1987) a much better relationship with organized psychiatry is developing. The third move was a strong initiative taken in 1978 by President George Lavatte. Once again a National Task Force on Organizational Development was established which, after cross-country consultation, developed a set of operating principles which clarified the mutually supportive roles and responsibilities of the three operating levels of the organization. These were formally approved by the membership at the annual meeting and, it was felt, they would maintain a unity of purpose while still allowing some diversity among consitituent elements, sufficient to give freedom to respond to local and regional needs and concerns. Thus this theme was reiterated for at least the third time.

In the meantime the CMHA continued to grow. A Mental Health Association in the Northwest Territories joined the National as the eleventh division in 1972, and in 1981 a group in the Yukon became the twelfth.

4. Closer Ties with Government

From time to time, there had been attempts in the past to establish close working relations with the federal government. Investigation showed, however, that the ordinary members of Parliament and senators seldom had much interest or specific knowledge about mental health affairs. President Henri Olivier felt that a special series of letters or bulletins should be prepared and distributed to this group. This was initiated in 1972. Shortly afterwards the new updated and comprehensive edition of the book *The Law and Mental Disorder* was published and presented personally to The Honourable Marc Lalonde, the federal Minister of Health and Welfare and to The Honourable

Otto Lang, the Minister of Justice. A strong working relationship was developed with the Law Reform Commission and important contributions were made to its various committees. The association continued to be involved in issues relating to fitness to stand trial, procedures required for the admission of patients to mental hospitals, and family law reform.

To provide even closer, day-to-day contact with the federal government, in 1977 Mrs. Mary Hagen of Ottawa was employed as Government Liaison Coordinator. Her task was to monitor the developments "on the hill" and keep the national office and the divisions informed about events of mental health significance. This project had to be discontinued after a year's trial because of budgetary problems.

Several important briefs on governmental policy and legislation were presented during the late 1970s and early 1980s. These included: brief to the Committee on Justice and Legal Affairs (1974); position statement on Federal Social Services Legislation (1977); submission to the Special Committee on the Handicapped and Disabled (1981); submission to the Royal Commission on the Economic Union and Develpment of Canada (1983); and, finally, a brief on elections which supported the right of mentally ill people to vote (1986). Many of these submissions and briefs, while directed to special committees and commissions of the federal government, required a careful preliminary review of existing provincial regulations and legislation. The amount of work entailed by both volunteers and staff in formulating and presenting these statements was really astounding.

5. A New Attack on Chronic Mental Illness

By the 1970s the mental hospitals were discharging increasing numbers of patients who were expected to live more or less independently in the community. Many of these people were continuing medication and in need of supervision. There did not seem to be sufficient appropriate housing accommodation available and the phenomenon of the "revolving door," where patients were constantly obliged to seek re-admission to hospitals only again to be quickly discharged, became familiar.

Volunteers from CMHA were no longer needed in the mental hospitals because the hospitals by that time had established their own volunteer groups after the pattern followed by general hospitals. Some hospitals were being demolished altogether or converted to other uses. Many CMHA members felt that this was a move in the right direction and was in line with the recommendations of the highly respected Tyhurst Report, *More for the Mind*. When that report was published, in 1963 the psychiatric bed capacity in Canada was 3.7 per 1000 population. In 1977 this had declined to 1.0 per 1000. Patients "on the books" had decreased from 79,707 to 24,362, a three-fold decrease. But, as Stephen Lurie[2] has shown in a brilliant study, this was a result of *trans*-institutionalization rather than *de*institutionalization. In other words, psychiatric units in general hospitals, special care facilities, and chronic care institutions had replaced the mental hospitals.

Many of the important recommendations of *More for the Mind*, such as the continuity of care extending into the community, had simply not developed adequately. Particularly tragic were the aging and chronic mentally ill persons who were living out their lives in isolation or in boarding homes for "special care," with little in the way of care or support.

The early 1980s brought significant progress in meeting the needs of the large population of disabled Canadians. In preparation for the U.N. International Year of Disabled Persons (1981), a special Parliamentary Committee issued a series of documents dealing with the broad areas of concern. A plan of action, including necessary legislative changes and provisions, was widely debated and endorsed. While the "mentally/psychiatrically disabled" were initially not included, the final wording of the Canadian Charter of Human Rights and Freedoms (1982) ensured that mental illness and disability were specifically covered as prohibited grounds for discrimination. This was a major landmark achievement in the long struggle for public acceptance of people suffering from mental disorders.

Stimulated by the increased public awareness and support for the needs of the disabled, CMHA's focus on the complex issues facing people with chronic mental disabilities was timely.

Dr. John Toews, a psychiatrist at the University of Manitoba, became prominent in the NSPC and eventually its chairman. Under his leadership, the Council urged the National Board to mount a major cross-country attack on the problem. Three resolutions, passed unanimously by the Board and membership at the annual meeting in 1983, lent considerable strength to the proposed program, (App. F). The first of these dealt with the need to intensify the Association's historically-strong advocacy stance ensuring the rights of persons with long-term mental disabilities to appropriate care, treatment and rehabilitation. The second dealt with the 1964 Charter of Health for Canadians which urged that all resources of the community be applied on an integrated approach toward improving the health of Canadians so that the continuity of care, comprehensive range of health services, and preventive activities could be provided. The third resolution dealt with the importance of unemployment as a stress factor having significant mental health implications. These three resolutions helped determine the direction of the programs at National for the next five years.

Several reports and books were produced enhancing these ideas; the first was *A Framework for Support* (1984). This book provided guidelines for the general public, especially community agencies and local branches of the CMHA, concerning people with severe mental health disabilities. In the following year came *Chronic Mental Health Disorders in Canada* (1985), a result of a nation-wide consultation jointly sponsored by the Ministry of Health and Welfare and the CMHA; *A Bibliography of Research Studies* (1986) containing annotated references of important studies published during the last ten years on the care of people with chronic mental illness, and two publications (1987), *From Consumer to Citizen* which documented the organization of a national network of people committed to the task of assisting in the community living of mentally disabled individuals, and *Listening*, an account of the experiences told in the words of people who have been (or are now) consumers of mental health services.

It is not surprising that, with so much emphasis placed by the association on community mobilization and social action, a new and, for some, strange-sounding vocabulary emerged. Words such as "animation," "adaptive planning," "empowering," "advocacy," and "thrust," all familiar and traditional words, now assumed a new and

252

enriched connotation in the framework of community action. With the expanded National Scientific Planning Council and with the emphasis on community organization, the need for a new name for the Council was considered. A change *was* made, but not a very major one. The NSPC now became the NS&PC (National Scientific *and* Planning Council) an indication of the importance attached to community planning and action in addition to medical and psycho-social study and research.

6. A New Approch to Prevention

An early attempt to mount a serious study on the prevention of mental illnesss had floundered in 1970. It was felt that the failure had been in part due to the attempt to think only in terms of organized public health and prevention medicine. The problem was obviously much too complex to respond to vaccines and simple hygienic measures. A new attack might now be possible if directed to the basic attitudes and behavioural patterns of the community. With the expanded NS&PC now establishing national committees with the funding from the federal government, foundations, and other sources, truly effective studies could be expected. This time the focus was firmly on prevention, and the first aspect to be tackled, as might be expected, was community action.

A working paper on *Primary Prevention* was produced in 1981; this was followed quickly in 1984 by the publication of a very important book, *Community Mental Health Action: Primary Prevention Programming in Canada*. This received excellent reviews and came to be regarded as a worthy successor to *More for the Mind*. Edited by Dr. D. Paul Lumsden of York University, this book was published by the Canadian Public Health Association. It contained articles, ranging from critical, stimulating essays written by over forty scientists and professionals to practical "how-to-do-it" guides. Publication of additional guidelines for establishing local preventive programs soon followed and several Canadian communities proceeded to implement them.

During the early 1980s there was increasing concern about unemployment. In 1982 the National Committee on Primary Prevention of the NS&PC organized a symposium on the mental health aspects of unemployment with an emphasis on what could be done to prevent the accompanying anxiety, stress, and tension from precipitating serious mental disorder. As we have seen, the National Board and the membership gave unanimous support to this task. By 1983 another important book was published, this time in a semi-popular format splendidly prepared by Dr. Sharon Kirsh. This book represented a co-ordinated effort by staff and volunteers across the country and was published with financial help from the Atkinson Charitable Foundation. It was called *Unemployment: Its Impact on Body and Soul* and it documented the psycho-physical damage to individuals and groups brought about by the inability to find jobs. It contained many helpful suggestions about retraining, developing skills in job finding, protecting one's personal, psychological and physical health.

While work on mental health and unemployment was progressing another project was spawned with its roots also in the Lumsden report, *Community Mental Health Action*. This one was concerned with how the job and workplace might have positive or negative aspects on mental health. This project quickly assumed major proportions with plans for study, survey, and research extending over the following five years, to terminate in 1987. It was planned and directed by an excellent committee on Mental Health and the Workplace chaired by Marvin Novick, Dean of Community Services at Ryerson Polytechnical Institute. The project received substantial support from the Ministry of Health and Welfare and is being watched carefully as a possible model for future strategy in mental health promotion.

Once again a popular summary was published by the association, *Work and Well-Being: The Changing Realities of Employment* (1984); and again, five local branches scattered across Canada became involved in action, research, and survey. Emerging implications of this study stressed the need to provide personal fulfillment through providing relief for the heavily pressured career-driven person, greater awareness of the psycho-social aspects of the job for the blue collar worker, equal opportunity for women workers, formal and informal support for the emotionally troubled worker and opportunity, or at least a vision of a more promising future for young workers.

7. International Activities in the 1980s

With such "animation" stimulating communities across our country, it is appropriate to bear in mind that mental health concerns are not limited to Canada. They constitute a world-wide problem and, as participation in the World Federation for Mental Health has so often shown, there are many countries, particularly in the Third World, which are struggling to improve their mental health services and are looking to Canada for help and support.

In 1983 at a biennial meeting of the WFMH, George Rohn met with a group from Zambia, Africa, which was eagerly seeking such help. After discussions with the Canadian International Development Agency (CIDA), assistance was obtained for the CMHA President Robert Martin and George Rohn to visit Africa to check the situation personally. As a result of this fact-finding visit, two projects were submitted to CIDA: to organize a nation-wide voluntary mental health association in Zambia and to acquire a small farm, outside of Harare in Zimbabwe, for a pilot rehabilitation program for discharged mental patients. This initial direct involvement of the CMHA in the Third World was supported by a CIDA grant of close to $200,000. Other African countries - Kenya, Botswana and Swaziland expressed interest in assistance from the CMHA for the development of community support for mental health programs and services. This is seen as a most appropriate helping relationship to be extended throughout South-Eastern Africa. Projects like these are helping to build respect for Canada among nations of the Third World.

8. New Patterns of Funding

A glance at the financial statements issued every year by the national association reveals that until the mid-fifties, the annual income varied between $25,000 and $50,000 (App. E). During the first few years the principal source of funds was private subscriptions, the generosity of a relatively few wealthy people. The annual grant from the federal government accounted for a sizeable portion, and grants from various institutions, particularly the large American Foundations, accounted for the rest. It should be remembered however, that foundations such as the Rockefeller, seldom made unconditional grants to voluntary associations. Most of the support negotiated by Hincks from this source for projects in Canada was given directly to the universities concerned.

The establishment of the provincial divisions and local

branches affected the national financial picture, particularly with respect to support from the United Way campaigns. An effort to report the annual financial position by consolidating all the support received at all levels began in 1955. During the next two decades, the total annual income rose from about $200,000 to well over two million dollars. From 1974 on, the annual financial statement reverted to an analysis of the national office receipts only, and in 1975 the income was about $300,000. It has risen steadily during the last ten years. In 1984, the last year for which figures are available, the income to the National Office was nearly $1,200,000. Much of this is accounted for by the large government grants made by the Ministry of Health and Welfare ($800,000 over the last five years) to finance such mental health promotion projects as *Mental Health in the Workplace* and *Mental Health Aspects of Unemployment*. One of the great problems however has been that while grants for special studies and projects were coming more easily, little if any money was available for national office administration.

The national office membership in the United Way of Metro Toronto was finally terminated in January 1986. By this time the annual grant from this source had amounted to nearly $80,000. In view of this, efforts were made as early as 1983 to organize a campaign to raise funds from public subscription. As long as the national office remained a member of the United Way, this was difficult; nevertheless amounts in the neighborhood of a hundred thousand dollars were raised annually.

Another problem appeared about this time. Several of the large teaching hospitals in Toronto began major fundraising campaigns for research and capital expansion, among them, the Clarke Institute of Psychiatry. To mount a broader national corporate appeal for psychiatric research, the campaign was conducted under the auspices of the Canadian Psychiatric Research Foundation (CPRF). Other neurological and psychiatric groups such as the Ontario Mental Health Foundation, Friends of Schizophrenics, Alzheimer's Society etc. also intensified their financial campaigns.

To minimize the potentially damaging competition and proliferation of appeals for "mental health", CPRF and CMHA have, in 1987, joined their campaigns through a separately-incorporated National Mental Health Fund. This first appeal for research, education and services, has raised some $800,000 which was divided between the two organizations.

In drawing attention to the major accomplishments of the thousands of men and women devoted to the cause of mental health in Canada during the last seventy years, the author feels he cannot improve on the words he wrote twenty-five years ago in the epilogue of the report *More for the Mind:*

> Mental Health transcends medical concern with sickness and health. It relates to the whole spectrum of organized social living. It has to do not only with spotting and treating children with mental health problems in the school, but with the whole fabric of the school itself. It has to do not only with the neurotic and character disorders of adults in the community, but with their marital, occupational and social needs. Thus the mental health problem of the community, while having an important psychiatric aspect, will not be resolved successfully by psychiatric planning alone. It will involve careful joint study and planning with many professional disciplines, including among others, psychology, education, social work, theology and the law.[3]

APPENDIX A

APPENDICES

NATIONAL PRESIDENTS
1918 - 1988

1918 - 37	Charles Ferdinand Martin	Montreal
1937 - 43	Sir Edward Wentworth Beatty	Montreal
1943 - 45	Morris W. Wilson	Montreal
1945 - 46	George Brock Chisholm	Ottawa
1946 - 55	Jonathan Campbell Meakins	Montreal
1955 - 61	John Stuart Donald Tory	Toronto
1961 - 64	Ian Ventress Dubienski	Winnipeg
1964 - 66	Murray Rankin	Halifax
1966 - 68	Gowan T. Guest	Vancouver
1968 - 70	Joseph F. O'Sullivan	Winnipeg
1970 - 72	Henri Olivier	Sorel
1972 - 74	Travis Wentworth Cushing	Saint John
1974 - 76	Eric J. Morris	Calgary
1976 - 78	Elspeth Hogg	Toronto
1978 - 80	George Lavatte	Sydney
1980 - 82	Richard Stephenson	Toronto
1982 - 84	Robert Andrews	St. John's
1984 - 86	Robert M. Martin	Winnipeg
1986 - 88	E. Austin Fricker	Waterloo
1988	Mary Oordt	Edmonton

APPENDIX B

CHAIRMEN OF NATIONAL SCIENTIFIC
COMMITTEES AND COUNCILS
1925 - 1988

1925 - 30	Prof. E.A. Bott Chairman of Research Committee
1930 - 40	Grant Fleming, M.D. Medical Director
1946 - 52	D. Ewen Cameron, M.D. Scientific Director
1953 - 54	D. Ewen Cameron, M.D. Chairman of National Scientific Planning Council
1954 - 56	D.G. McKerracher, M.D. Chairman of National Scientific Planning Council
1956 - 58	Burdett McNeel, M.D. Chairman of National Scientific Planning Council
1958 - 62	Robert O. Jones, M.D. Chairman of National Scientific Planning Council
1962 - 66	Charles A. Roberts, M.D. Chairman of National Scientific Planning Council
1966 - 70	Keith Yonge, M.D. Chairman of National Scientific Planning Council
1971 - 72	Thomas Boag, M.D. Chairman of National Scientific Planning Council
1973 - 77	Harry Prosen, M.D. Chairman of National Scientific Planning Council
1978 - 79	Quentin Rae-Grant, M.D. Chairman of National Scientific Planning Council
1979 - 83	Robert Martin, Ph.D. Chairman of National Scientific Planning Council
1984 - 85	John Toews, M.D. Chairman of National Scientific Planning Council
1985 - 86	Leonard Levine, M.S.W. Chairman of National Scientific Planning Council
1986 - 88	Jean Moore, Ph.D. Chairman of National Scientific Planning Council

APPENDIX C

SENIOR NATIONAL STAFF OFFICERS
1918 - 1988

1918 - 24	C.K. Clarke Medical Director
1918 - 20	C.M. Hincks Secretary
1920 - 24	C.M. Hincks Associate Medical Director
1924 - 26	C.M. Hincks Medical Director
1926 - 52	C.M. Hincks General Director
1918 - 20	Marjorie Keyes Field Worker
1920 - 52	Marjorie Keyes Secretary
1920 - 24	Gordon Mundie Associate Medical Director
1924 - 33	J.G. McKay Associate Medical Director
1926 - 31	D.M. Le Bourdais Director of Education and Publicity
1930 - 40	Grant Fleming Medical Director
1931 - 35	H.B. Spaulding Director of Statistics and Registration
1931 - 40	C.B. Farrar Associate Medical Director
1932 - 35	A.H. Desloges Director of Quebec Affairs
1932 - 35	Helen Reid Director of Immigration
1936 - 38	John D.M. Griffin Director of Education and Mental Health
1938 - 41	John D.M. Griffin Associate Medical Director
1945 - 52	John D.M. Griffin Medical Director

262

1952 - 71	John D.M. Griffin General Director
1950 - 52	Reva Gerstein Director of Education
1952 - 58	Reva Gerstein Director of Program Planning
1955 - 62	Alvan Gamble Director of Public Relations
1956 - 60	Edmund Johnstone Director of Personnel and Finances
1958 - 60	George Rohn Director of Program and Development
1960 - 71	George Rohn Director of Administration
1962 - 73	Leonard Crainford Director of Communications
1971 - 87	George Rohn General Director
1970 - 81	Hilda Mackow Assistant Director
1971 - 77	John Clayton Director of Professional Development
1977 - 78	Julie Rose Director of Planning and Development
1975 -	Jeannine Hurd Director of Administration
1979 -	Gordon Morwood National Program Director
1985 -	Paul Winnell Director of Resource Development
1987 -	Edward Pennington General Director
1988 -	Linda Egan Communications Co-ordinator

APPENDIX D

PRESIDENTS AND EXECUTIVE OFFICERS
PROVINCIAL AND TERRITORIAL DIVISIONS
AS OF JUNE 30, 1988

BRITISH COLUMBIA   Charter   October 6, 1952
President: Dr. David Spiers
Executive Director: Ms. Chloe Lapp
                                692 East 26th Avenue
                                Vancouver, British Columbia
                                V5V 2H7

ALBERTA   Charter   February 7, 1955
President: Dr. Jim Browne
Executive Director: Mr. Ron LaJeunesse
                                328 Capital Place
                                9707 - 110 Street
                                Edmonton, Alberta
                                T5K 2L9

SASKATCHEWAN   Charter   November 27, 1950
President: Mr. Robert Burrage
Executive Director: Mr. Dennis Exner
                                1810 Albert Street
                                Regina, Saskatchewan
                                S4P 2S8

MANITOBA   Charter   February 13, 1953
President: Ms. Sharon Mulder
Executive Director: Mr. William Martin
                                2 - 836 Ellice Avenue
                                Winnipeg, Manitoba
                                R3G 0C2

ONTARIO   Charter   October 6, 1952
President: Mr. Peter Benson
Executive Director: Mr. Howard Richardson
                                56 Wellesley Street West
                                4th Floor
                                Toronto, Ontario
                                M5S 2S3

QUEBEC   Charter   February 7, 1955
President: Dr. Michele Counsineau
Executive Director: M. Michel Trottier
                                     550 Sherbrooke Street West
                                     Suite 310
                                     Montreal, P.Q.
                                     H3A 1B9

NEW BRUNSWICK   Charter   November 7, 1950
President: Ms. Velma Wade
Executive Director: Mr. Kenneth Ross
                                     55 Brunswick Street
                                     Fredericton, New Brunswick
                                     E3B 1G5

NOVA SCOTIA   Charter   November 27, 1950
President: Mr. John Mroz
Executive Director: Mr. Douglas Crossman
                                     5739 Inglis Street
                                     Halifax, Nova Scotia
                                     B3H 1K5

PRINCE
EDWARD ISLAND   Charter   December 16, 1959
President: Mr. Jay MacDonald
Executive Director: Mr. Allan James
                                     96 Sydney Street
                                     P.O. Box 785
                                     Charlottetown, Prince Edward Island
                                     C1A 7L9

NEWFOUNDLAND   Charter   May 28, 1964
President: Mr. Arthur Sullivan
Executive Director: Mr. Tom Fowler
                                     93 Water Street
                                     P.O. Box 5788
                                     St. John's, Newfoundland
                                     A1C 1A5

NORTHWEST
TERRITORIES   Charter   September 1972
President: Rev. Gerry Mitchinson
Executive Director: Mr. Marino Casebeer
                                     P.O. Box 2580
                                     Yellowknife, Northwest Territories
                                     X1A 2P9

YUKON
President:

Charter   June 1981
Mr. Charles Pugh
8 Green Crescent
Whitehorse, Yukon
Y1A 4R9

NO STAFF

THE CANADIAN MENTAL HEALTH
ASSOCIATION ANNUAL INCOME
BY FIVE -YEAR INTERVALS

(in 1000s)

YEAR	I NOMINAL AMOUNT (in $)	CP INDEX	II 1985 DOLLARS
1920	45	22.9	250
1925	24	18.4	166
1930	90	18.4	623
1935	50	14.7	433
1940	40	16.1	316
1945	32	18.4	221
1950	50	25.2	252
1955	47	28.5	210
1960	120	31.4	485
1965	131	34.0	490
1970	218	41.0	676
1975	260	58.5	565
1980	461	88.9	660
1985	1,120	127.2	1,120

The increasing amounts after 1955 reflect the National Office share of funds raised by the rapidly developing provincial divisions. The very rapid increase after 1975 reflects the increasing involvement of the federal government and foundations in providing grants for expanding national programs. Very little of this money could be used to defray adminstrative costs of the National Office. The apparent affluence of the 1980s is therefore somewhat misleading.•

• The constant values were kindly calculated by Deloitte, Haskins & Sells, the accountant for the National office, CMHA.

NATIONAL BOARD RESOLUTIONS 1980
RESOLUTION #1. ADVOCACY AND PERSONS WITH LONG-TERM MENTAL DISABILITIES

This resolution is made to the Canadian Mental Health Association at its annual general meeting in St. John's, Newfoundland, August 1983, sponsored by the national Mental Health Services Committee.

Whereas: The future of mental health care in Canada is currently uncertain, and,

Whereas: The growth of community based mental health care is threatened by such diverse factors as fiscal restraint, neighbourhood opposition, professionals' protectionism and escalating costs, and,

Whereas: We are running the risk of a retreat back to institutional care, wherein the major gains of community care are being threatened, and,

Whereas: The group most endangered by the current uncertainty over the future of mental health care is the long-term mentally disabled.

Be it therefore resolved:

- That the Canadian Mental Health Association intensify its historically strong advocacy stance at the national and branch levels to ensure that the rights of persons with long-term mental disabilities to appropriate care, treatment and rehabilitation, are restored.

- That the Canadian Mental Health Association actively alert municipal, provincial/territorial and federal levels of government to the plight of the long-term mentally disabled and monitor the activities of all relevant government departments to ensure that appropriate action is taken to improve the quality of life of this population.

- That the Canadian Mental Health Assocation undertake a public education campaign to sensitize the nation to the needs and capacities of persons with mental disabilities and to combat the stigma associated with these disabilities.

- That the Canadian Mental Health Association develop and demonstrate volunteer and community based programs which foster community involvement in finding solutions to problems faced by persons with mental disabilities.

- That the Canadian Mental Health Association encourage the development of professional education courses on the care and rehabilitation of the long-term mentally disabled.

- That the Canadian Mental Health Association maintain a stance in support of additional basic and applied research into chronic disorders.

- That the Canadian Mental Health Association actively foster the development of consumer self-help groups as part of the overall strategy for change, and,

- That the Canadian Mental Health Association expand its efforts to recruit qualified persons, who have been mentally ill, as members of national committees and for other leadership roles to assist the association in its promotional and developmental programs.

RESOLUTION #2. MENTAL HEALTH SERVICES - CANADA HEALTH ACT

This resolution is made to the Canadian Mental Health Association at its annual general meeting in St. John's, Newfoundland, August 1983, sponsored by the National Management Committee.

Whereas: The care of the mentally ill is one of the major health problems of our time; and,

Whereas: Discrimination and distinction persists in the organization and provision of hospital care and community health care for the mentally ill; and,

Whereas: The current federal/provincial debate on the future cost-sharing and financing of health and social services (Canada Health Act 1983) will have a direct impact on the quality of mental health services in Canada;

Be it therefore resolved:

- That the membership of the Canadian Mental Health Association re-endorse the goals and principles of the 1964 Charter of Health for Canadians;

- That the Canadian Mental Health Association work actively to support the maintenace of a health care insurance system in which the principles of universal access, uniform terms and conditions, comprehensiveness, portability and public administration are upheld;

- That the federal government be encouraged to make health and social service funding to provinces conditional upon the implementations of these principles;

- That the federal government be encouraged to provide the full funding originally agreed to at the time that provincial health grants were set up to allow implementation of these principles; and,

- That we encourage the addition of another goal to those originally listed in the 1964 Charter, namely that the maximum use of all resources in the community be applied in an **integrated** approach to improving the health care of all Canadians so that **continuity of care** and a **comprehensive range of services** would be provided. Health insured services should include prevention programs, early problem identification, treatment, aftercare and rehabilitation.

Please note:

Wherever the word province is used, this denotes all provinces and territories.

RESOLUTION #3. MENTAL HEALTH AND UNEMPLOYMENT

This resolution is made to the Canadian Mental Health Association at its annual general meeting in St. John's, Newfoundland, August, 1983, sponsored by the National Working Committee on the human impact of unemployment and the National Primary Prevention Committee.

Whereas: The New Brunswick Division has spoken out publicly on mental health impacts of unemployment; and,

Whereas: Important National committees of the Canadian Mental Health Association (National Board, National Scientific & Planning Council, Primary Prevention Committee) have supported and taken initiative in regard to expressed concerns;

Whereas, it is now recognized:

- That unemployment and poverty are of utmost and urgent concern to virtually all members of Canadian society.

- That unemployed persons may lack the economic resources to fulfill their own or their dependents' physical requirements for food, clothing, and shelter: such circumstances are exceedingly stressful.

- That unemployed persons may lose their sense of self-worth and belonging, within the context of their family, their former workplace and their community.

- That unemployed persons, oppressed by fear and frustration, can muster energy merely to survive, not to thrive and bloom.

- That the most seriously disadvantaged (e.g., the long-term chronically mentally disabled) may suffer doubly under current economic conditions in that insufficient priority is given to meeting their needs and that opportunities for vocational preparation and employment virtually disappear.

- That unemployment is not in the majority of cases, the fault of the individual; rather, it is a phenomenon that grows out of a system and therefore, it can be eradicated only if changes to the system are implemented; blaming or changing the individual will not make the problem disappear; and,

Whereas: The fact of unemployment raises not only economic questions, but also moral questions about the relationship between people and production; and,

Whereas: The issue of unemployment is of particular importance to the
Assocation in that it identifies aspects of mental health problems
that can be dealt with in a pro-active and prevention oriented
manner;

Be it therefore resolved:

That the membership of the Canadian Mental Health Association
sets as a goal for itself the development and implementation of a
nation-wide animation and public advocacy process that aims at
the prevention of mental health problems through sound economic and social development policies.

272

MAJOR PUBLICATIONS PRODUCED OR SPONSORED BY THE CANADIAN MENTAL HEALTH ASSOCIATION 1918 - 1986

Canadian Journal of Mental Hygiene. Published quarterly by the Canadian National Committee for Mental Hygiene 1919-1922

Smith, W.G. *A study on Canadian immigration.* Toronto; Ryerson Press, 1920

Mental hygiene of childhood: lectures by various international authorities in celebration of the tenth anniversary of the founding of the Canadian National Committee for Mental Hygiene. Toronto; The Committee, 1928

Young, C.H. *The Ukranian Canadians.* Toronto; Thomas Nelson, 1931

The Canadian National Committee for Mental Hygiene: a report of a survey of the organisation made by the Canadian Medical Association. Edited by Fitzgerald and Fleming. Ottawa; Metropolitan Life Insurance, 1932

Griffin, J.D., Line, W. and Laycock, S.R. *Mental Hygiene: a manual for teachers.* Toronto; Gage & Co., 1937

Young, C.H. and Reid, H.R.Y. *The Japanese Canadians.* Toronto; University of Toronto Press, 1939

Hoadley, G. *A study of the distribution of medical care and public health services.* Toronto; CNCMH, 1939. QSMHC Archives

Chisholm, G.B., *Morale: a platoon commander's responsility.* Toronto; CMCMH, 1941. QSMHC Archives

Hincks, Clarence M. *Toronto's psychiatric services: report of a survey made by the Canadian National Committee for Mental Hygiene.* Toronto; Toronto Welfare Chest, 1945

Biographical directory of physicians engaged in psychiatry in Canada. Toronto; Canadian National Committee for Mental Hygiene, 1950

Gerstein, Reva et al. *Milestones in mental health: an outline of the major accomplishments of the CNCMH over the past forty years.* Toronto; The Committee, 1958

Tyhurst, J.S. et al. *More for the mind: a study of psychiatric services in Canada.* Toronto; Canadian Mental Health Association, 1963

Chalke, F.C.R. et al. *The law and mental disorder: hospitals and patient care.* Toronto; Canadian Mental Health Association, 1964 (part 1 of 3 part series on law and mental disorders)

Chalke, F.C.R. et al. *The law and mental disorder: civil rights and privileges.* Toronto; Canadian Mental Health Association, 1967 (Part 2 of 3 part series on law and mental disorders)

Chalke, F.C.R. et al. *The law and mental disorder: criminal process.* Toronto; Canadian Mental Health Association, 1969 (part 3 of 3 part series on law and mental disorders)

Swadron, B., and Sullivan, D.R. *The law and mental disorder.* revised and edited by Barry Swadron and D. R. Sullivan. Toronto; Canadian Mental Health Association, 1973

King, M.R. *One million children: a national study of Canadian children with emotional and learning disorders.* Toronto; Leonard Crainford, 1970 for CELDIC.

Rae-Grant, Q. and Moffat, P. *Residential care for Canadian children.* Toronto; Leonard Crainford, 1971 for CMHA.

Ban, T.A. and Lehmann, H.E. *Nicotinic acid in the treatment of schizophrenia.* Progress report 1. Toronto; Canadian Mental Health Association, 1970

Experience and experiment: a collection of essays, Shamsie, J. ed. (sponsored by the Canadian Mental Health Association, The Hospital for Sick Children and Thistletown Regional Centre) Leonard Crainford, Toronto 1977

Probings: sixty mini essays on mental health by Canadian leaders. edited by Leonard Crainford, Toronto; Leonard Crainford, 1968 for CMHA.

Contributions to primary prevention: a collection of conceptual papers. Toronto; National Scientific Planning Council, CMHA, 1981

Lamsden, P. *Community mental health action.* Toronto; Canadian Mental Health Association, 1981

Unemployment: its impact on body and soul. Toronto; The CMHA, 1983

Work and well-being: cross country perspectives on mental health and the work place. Toronto; The CMHA 1984

Chronic mental disorders in Canada: a needs assessement project and report of a national symposium convened by the CMHA. Ottawa; Department of National Health and Welfare, 1982

The chronic mental patient: selective annotated bibliography of psychiatric literature 1970-1980. Toronto; The CMHA, 1984

A framework for support for people with severe mental disabilities. Toronto; CMHA, 1984

Listening to people who have directly experienced the mental health system. Toronto; The CMHA, 1985

From consumer to citizen: creating a national network for mental health advocacy. Toronto; The CMHA, 1986

Forum: a newsletter concerned with people who have severe mental disabilities. Toronto; The CMHA, 1986

REFERENCES

CHAPTER I

1. Griffin, J.D. and Greenland, C. Manifestations of madness in New France. Actes, XXV Congres international histoire de la medicine Quebec 1976, p. 727.

2. Griffin., J.D. and Greenland, C. *Canadian psychiatry: a documentary history.* (unpublished) Vol. 1 Chap. VII QSMHC Archives.

3. Griffin, J.D. and Greenland, C. *op.cit.*

4. Jones, K. *A history of the mental health services.* Routledge and Keagan Paul, London 1972, p. 235.

5. Minutes of the inaugural meeting of the Nova Scotia League for the Protection of the Feeble-Minded, June 4, 1908, p. 1. Archives, Nova Scotia Division, CMHA. In 1920 it expanded its objectives and became the Mental Hygiene Society and finally the Nova Scotia Division of the Canadian Mental Health Association.

6. Stead, Mrs. The Nova Scotia League for the care and protection of the feeble minded. *Public Health Journal* (Can) 1944, 5: 4: 219.

7. MacMurchy, H. 9th Annual report on the feeble minded, in *47th Annual Report of the Inspectors of Prisons and Charitable Institutions in Ontario,* 1914.

8. Clarke, C.K. A history of the Toronto General Hospital psychiatric clinic *Canadian Journal of Mental Hygiene* 1921, 1:1: 30.

9. Griffin, J.D. and Greenland, C. *Canadian psychiatry: a documentary history* .(unpublished) Vol. 2, Ontario 1867-1914 QSMHC Archives.

10. Greenland, C. The treatment of the mentally retarded in Ontario. *Canadian Psychiatric Association Journal* 1963, 8:5:328.

11. Hodgins, F.E. *Royal Commission Report: The care and control of the mental defectives and feeble minded in Ontario. Kings Printer,* Oct. 1919.

12. Beers, C.W. *A mind that found itself: an autobiography.* Longmans Green & Co. (1st edition) New York 1908.

13. Cook, G. Mental hygiene. *American Journal of Insanity* 1859, 15:3 and 4:272-353.

14. Ray, Isaac. *Mental hygiene.* Ticknor & Fields, Boston 1863.

15. Workman, J. Discussion of Dr. Ray's paper on mental hygiene. *American Journal of Insantity* 1858, 15:1:123.

16. Letter: CMA to Griffin, Feb. 1980 QSMHC Archives.

17. Young, E.H. Report of the convention of societies for mental hygiene. *Bulletin of the Ontario Hospitals for the Insane* 1914, 7:4, 236.

18. Hincks, C.M. *Prospecting for mental health: an autobiography* (unpublished) p. 29 QSMHC Archives.

19. *The Toronto Star*, Aug. 23, 1913.

20. Griffin, J.D. The amazing careers of Hincks and Beers. *Canadian Journal of Psychiatry* 1982, 27:668-671.

21. Fitzgerald, J.G. and Fleming G. *Report of a survey of the Canadian National Committee for Mental Hygiene by the Canadian Medical Association, 1932.* (Henceforth referred to as the Fitzgerald-Fleming Report 1932) QSMHC Archives.

22. *Clarence Meredith Hincks, 1885-1964: A Recollection.* Long-play recording produced for the CMHA by the CBC. (In his memoirs Dr. Hincks recalls one early meeting of this kind during which $24,000 was raised in three minutes!)

23. Hincks autobiography *op. cit.* p.p. 33-4.

CHAPTER II

1. Mental hygiene survey of the Province of Manitoba 1918. (confidential report,) CNCMH 1919 QSMHC Archives.

2. Hincks autobiography *op. cit.*

3. Confidential report *op. cit.*

4. Hincks autobiography *op. cit.*

5. Confidential report *op. cit.*

6. Hopkins, J.C. *The Canadian annual review of public affairs 1919* Toronto 1920, pp. 728-46.

7. Roland, C.G. Clarence Hincks in Manitoba, 1918. *Manitoba Medical Review* 1966, 46:2:107-13.

8. Letter: Hincks to Beers, March 15, 1919 QSMHC Archives

9. *Prince Edward Island Journal of the Legislative Assembly,* 1875 App.G.

10. Nova Scotia, Supplementary evidence as to the management of the hospital for the insane, Halifax, 1872. Nova Scotia, legislative library.

11. Now in the museum of the London Psychiatric Hospital.

12. Hincks autobiography *op. cit.*

13. Hincks autobiography *op. cit.*

14. Farrar, C.B. I remember C.K. Clarke. *American Journal of Psychiatry* 1957, 114:4.

15. Clarke, C.K. and Farrar, C.B. One thousand psychiatric cases from the Canadian army. *Canadian Journal of Mental Hygiene* 1920, p.p.1,4,313.

16. Fitzgerald-Fleming Report 1932, p. 10.

17. Hastings, C.J.O. Report of the Board of Health, City of Toronto, Aug. 1920 City of Toronto Archives.

18. Pratt, E.J. The application of the Binet-Simon tests to a Toronto Public School. *Canadian Journal of Mental Hygiene* 1921, 3:1.

19. Pratt, E.J. Mental measurement as applied to a Toronto school. *Public Health Journal* (Can.) 1921, 12:4:148.

20. Mental hygiene survey of Ontario schools. CNCMH 1920-24 (unpublished reports) QSMHC Archives.

21. Morphy, A.G., and Tait, W.J. Mental hygiene survey of Montreal Protestant schools. *Canadian Journal of Mental Hygiene* 1921, 3:1.

22. Letter: Hastings to Hincks, Apr. 20, 1929 QSMHC Archives.

CHAPTER III

1. See Chap. IV, Sec. 4

2. *Royal commission on mental hygiene.* Province of British Columbia, final report. Dec. 30, 1925 pp. 66-7 QSMHC Archives.

3. Blatz, W.E. and Bott, E.A. Behavior of public school children: a description of method. No. 1 in Studies in mental hygiene of children. *The Pedagogical`Seminary and Journal of Genetic Psychology* 1927, 34:4:552-82.

4. Bott, E.A. in *Twenty-five years of child study.* Bernhardt, K. et al. eds. University of Toronto Press, Toronto 1951., p. 16-7.

5. Bott, E.A. *op.cit.* p. 28.

6. Fitzgerald-Fleming Report 1932, pp. 22-3.

7. Volpe, R. A Piagetian perspective on life span development. in *Piagetian theory in the helping professions*. Margery, J. ed., University of California Press, Los Angeles 1981, vol. II, pp. 283-287.

8. Volpe R. Longterm meaning of severe corporal punishment. *International Journal of Child Abuse and Neglect,* (in press).

9. Bott, E.A., Chant, S.N.F. and McPhee, E. *Studies in industrial psychology* University of Toronto Press, Toronto 1920.

10. Ketchum, J.D. Boys gangs and mental hygiene. *The CNCMH Bulletin* 1930, 5:1 and 5:4 QSMHC Archives.

11. Line W. Educational progress *Mental Health Bulletin* 1931, 6:3 and 6:5 QSMHC Archives.

12. Hutchinson, P.P. *The Mental Hygiene Institute, the development and work - 1919-68*. Montreal, MHI 1970.

13. Annual Report CNCMH 1925 QSMHC Archives.

14. Annual Report *op. cit.*

15. Annual Report CNCMH 1929 QSMHC Archives.

CHAPTER IV

1. Hart, B. *The psychology of insanity*. Cambridge University Press 1925.

2. Tredgold, A.F. *Mental deficiency.* (fifth edn.) Boilliere, Tindall and Cox, London 1929, pp. 501-2.

3. Tredgold, A.F. The sterilization of mental defectives. *Mental Welfare,* April 1925. (Reprinted in part in *CNCMH Bulletin* 1926).

4. Hincks autobiography *op. cit.* pp. 27-8.

5. QSMHC Archives.

6. Mental hygiene of childhood: a series of lectures celebrating the tenth anniversary of the founding of the Canadian National Committee for Mental Hygiene. 1928 QSMHC Archives.

7. Personal conversations: Hincks and Keyes with Griffin.

8. Letter: Hincks to W.L.M. King, Jan. 8, 1924 QSMHC Archives.

CHAPTER V

1. Bullis, H.E. *Chance encounters: an autobiography.* Academy Books, Rutland, Vt. 1970, pp. 102-5.

2. Letter: Bullis to J.D.Griffin., QSMHC Archives.

3. Hincks autobiography *op. cit.*

4. Ebaugh, F.G. and Rymer, C.A. *Psychiatry in medical education.* The Commonwealth Fund, New York 1942.

5. Hincks autobiography *op. cit.* QSMHC Archives.

6. Hincks *Ibid.*

7. Griffin, J.D., Laycock, S. and Line, W. *Mental hygiene: a manual for teachers.* Gage & co., Toronto 1937.

8. *Shyness in children.* A documentary film produced by the National Film Board in its mental health series 1938.

9. Birmingham, M. Hormonal response to stress, in *Research at the Allan Memorial Institute,* Skelton-Passmore E., ed., AMI 1976.

CHAPTER VI

1. Fitzgerald - Fleming Report 1932.

2. Griffin, Laycock and Line *op. cit.*

3. Hall, G.E. et al. Physiological studies in experimental insulin and metrazol shock. *American Journal of Psychiatry* 1938, pp. 95, 563. (Read by invitation at the Annual Meeting of the American Psychiatric Association, San Francisco June 1938.

4. Hincks autobiography *op. cit.*

CHAPTER VII

1. McCullough, J.S.W. The relation of psychiatry to public health. *Public Health Journal* (Can.) 1915, 6:4: 186.

2. Smith, W. Psychology and public health. *Public Health Journal* (Can.) 1918, 9:3:106.

3. Griffin, Laycock and Line *op. kit.*

4. Seeley, J.R. et al. *Crestwood Heights.* University of Toronto Press, Toronto 1956.

5. Chisholm, G.B. The psychiatry of enduring peace and social progress. *Psychiatry* 1946, 9: 144.

6. Cameron, D.E. Early schizophrenia. *American Journal of Psychiatry* 1938, 95:567.

7. Hincks, C.M. Review of dementia praecox undertakings supported by the Scottish Rite Masons. (33 A.A. Northern Jurisdiction, U.S.A.)

Address to the open meeting of the Committee on Benevolence, Chicago, September 23, 1941 QSMHC Archives.

8. Griffin, J.D.M. Occupational therapy in the Ontario Orthopaedic Hospital. *Canadian Journal of Occupational Therapy and Physiotherapy* 1938, 5:1:3.

9. Young, C.H. *The Ukranian Canadians*. Thomas Nelson & Sons, Toronto 1931.

10. Young, C.H. and Reid, H.R.Y. *The Japanese Canadians*. University of Toronto Press, Toronto 1939.

11. Agnew, H. The medical survey of Canada. *Canadian Medical Associaton Journal* 1931, 24:123.

12. Hincks, C.M. *Report on public administration in Canada, 1934* (unpublished). A study financed by the Spelman Fund, New York QSMHC Archives.

13. Annual Report CNCMH 1939 QSMHC Archives.

14. Hoadley, G. *A study of the distribution of medical care and public health services*. CNCMH 1939 QSMHC Archives.

CHAPTER VIII

1. Feasby, W.R. *Official history of the Canadian medical services 1939-45*. Ottawa, Edmond Cloutier 1956, Vol. II p. 57.

2. *Medical department of the United States army in the World War*, Washington, U.S. Govt. Printing Office 1929.

3. QSMHC Archives (CMHA Collection).

4. Hincks autobiography op. cit. p. 131.

5. *American Journal of Psychiatry* Jan. 1941, 97:4.

6. Line, W. and Griffin, J.D.M. Personnel selection in the army. *Canadian Medical Association Journal* 1943, 48:394.

7. Griffin, J.D.M. and McKerracher, D.G. Psychiatry in the Canadian army. *American Journal of Psychiatry* July 1943, 100:1:137.

8. Annual Report to the National Board of Directors 1942 QSMHC Archives.

9. Annual Report 1944.

10. H. Spencer Clark in interview with David McLeod on the history of the Guild Inn. University of Waterloo Library & Archives.

11. Blatz, W.E. *Understanding the young child.* University of London Press, London 1944. Foreword, pp. vii-ix.

12. Annual Report 1942 *op. cit.*

13. Annual Report *ibid.*

14. Annual Report to the National Board of Directors 1944 QSMHC Archives.

15. Laycock, S.R. A mental hygiene survey of Canadian education 1944. (unpublished) QSMHC Archives.

16. Annual Report to the National Board of Directors 1944 *op. cit.*

17. Annual Report to the National Board of Directors 1945.

CHAPTER IX

1. Hincks, C.M. Toronto's psychiatric resources. United Welfare Chest, Toronto 1945 QSMHC Archives.

2. Boys, J.F. The birth of a community mental health clinic. Thesis for M.S.W., University of Toronto 1953.

3. Briault, M.A. History of the Toronto Mental Health Clinic, 1946-54. Thesis for M..S.W., University of Toronto 1954.

CHAPTER X

1. Annual Report to the National Board of Directors 1945 QSMHC Archives.

2. Annual Report 1948.

3. Hincks, C.M. memorandum to National Board 1945.

4. Annual Report 1945.

5. See Chapter IX.

6. Annual Report 1947.

7. Annual Report 1948.

8. Laird, I. and Whitley, H. *Mental health in education: an evaluation of the special mental health training of selected teachers.* CMHA 1954 QSMHC Archives.

9. Griffin, J.D. and Seeley, J.R. Education for mental health: an experiment. *Canadian Education* 1952, 7:3.

10. Seeley, J.R. et al. *Crestwood Heights.* University of Toronto Press, Toronto 1956.

11. Griffin, J.D. and Seeley, J.R. *op. cit.*

12. Report of survey of the Hospital for Mental and Nervous Diseases, St. Johns, Newfoundland and of the problem of mental deficiency among Newfoundland school children. Submitted by the National Commmittee for Mental Hygiene (Canada), October 1948.

CHAPTER XI

1. *Proceedings. International congress on mental health, London 1948.* Columbia University Press, New York 1948 QSMHC Archives.

2. Annual Report to the National Board of Directors 1948 QSMHC Archives.

3. Report of the International Preparatory Commission, in *Proceedings of 1948 congress op. cit.*

CHAPHER XII

1. Minutes of the Scientific Planning Committee, NCMH(C) 1951 QSMHC Archives.

2. Annual Report to the National Board of Directors 1950.

CHAPTER XIII

1. Personal communication: Keyes to Griffin 1958.

2. Rohn, G. Special report to the National Board of Directors on the White Cross Centres, 1959 QSMHC Archives.

3. *Brief to the Royal Commission on Canada's economic prospects.* CMHA, April 1956 QSMHC Archives.

4. *Royal Commission on Canada's economic projects: final report* Queens Printer 1957.

5. Tyhurst, J.S. et al. *More for the mind: a study of psychiatric services in Canada.* CMHA, Toronto 1963 QSMHC Archives.

6. Griffen, J.D. More for the mind: the Canadian Mental Health Associations report and its implications. *American Journal of Psychiatry* Nov. 1964, 121:5.

7. *Action for mental health: Final report of the Joint Commission on Mental Health.* NAMH, New York 1962 QSMHC Archives.

8. CMHA brief to the Royal Commission on Health Services, May 1952 QSMHC Archives.

9. Roberts, C.A. The organization and administration of psychiatric services in Canada *Psychiatric Journal*, University of Ottawa. June 1980,5:2

10. Sim, A. The mental health consultants in the school. *William Line Memorial Seminar* (unpublished) QSMHC Archives.

CHAPTER XIV

1. Minutes of the NSPC of the CMHA 1957 and 1958 QSMHC Archives.

2. *The unfettered researcher; a report on a new system of research support.* CMHA, Toronto 1965 QSMHC Archives.

3. Feasibility study: a campaign for funding an endowment fund for research. G.A. Brakeley Co. Ltd. for the CMHA, May 1959 QSMHC Archives.

4. Ban, T.A., and Lehmann, H.E. *Nicotinic acid and the treatment of schizophrenia, progress reports I, II and III*. CMHA Toronto 1970 and 1971 QSMHC Archives.

CHAPTER XV

1. Line, W. *Canadian Medical Association Journal*, Dec. 1954, 71:6:626-7.

2. Annual Report of the General Director CMHA 1958.

CHAPTER XVI

1. Chalke, C.F.R. et al. The law and mental disorder. *I Hospitals and patient care 1964, II Civil rights and privileges 1967, and III Criminal process 1969*. CMHA, Toronto QSMHC Archives.

2. Swadron, B.B. and Sullivan, D.R. *The law and mental disorder*. (revised and re-edited) CMHA, Toronto 1973.

3. *One million children: a national study of Canadian children with emotional and learning disorders*. Published for CELDIC by Leonard Crainford, Toronto 1970.

4. Rae-Grant, Q. and Moffat, P. *Children in residential care*. CMHA, Toronto, 1971.

CHAPTER XVII

(no references)

CHAPTER XVIII

1. Annual Report of the General Director 1958.

2. Annual Report of the General Director 1969.

CHAPTER XIX

1. Letter :Clayton to Griffin, Jan. 1978 QSMHC Archives.

2. Lurie, S. Mental health services in Canada: More for the mind — have we got less? *in Issues in Canadian Human Services.* Etd. by Nair, M.D., Hain, R.C. and Draper, J.A. OISE Toronto, 1964.

3. *More for the mind op. cit.*

NOMINAL INDEX

288